winning
weight training

winning
weight training

Jim Murray

Contemporary Books, Inc.
Chicago

Library of Congress Cataloging in Publication Data

Murray, Jim.
   Winning Weight Training.

   Includes index.
    1. Weight lifting.   2. Physical fitness.
3. Physical education and training.
1. Title.
GV546.M86   1982   796.4'1   81-69625
ISBN 0-8092-5818-8   AACR2
ISBN 0-8092-5824-2 (pbk.)

Hugh Pritchard took most of the exercise pictures in this book.
Others, with credits noted in the captions, were taken by Bruce
Klemens.

The photos of Mike Webster and Jon Kolb were kindly provided by
Joe Gordon of the Pittsburgh Steelers; the picture of Russ Hodge
was provided by the Athletic News Bureau of UCLA; and the
discus-throwing photo of Jon Cole (taken by Charles Conley) was
provided by Arizona State University.

Published by Contemporary Books, Inc.
180 North Michigan Avenue, Chicago, Illinois 60601
Manufactured in the United States of America
Library of Congress Catalog Card Number: 81-69625
International Standard Book Number: 0-8092-5818-8 (cloth)
                              0-8092-5824-2 (paper)

Published simultaneously in Canada by
Beaverbooks, Ltd.
150 Lesmill Road
Don Mills, Ontario M3B 2T5
Canada

This book is dedicated to good training buddies over the years . . .

. . . in the 1940s:
  Jim Lorimer, Bob Neeld, Charlie Farkas, Reed Pratt, Dick Anderson, Ted Ediss, Frank Thropp

. . . the 1950s, at York, Pennsylvania:
  John Grimek, Steve Stanko, John Terpak Sr. and Jr., Jules Bacon, Yas Kuzuhara, Bob Hoffman, Joe Pitman, Pete Marozas, Paul Anderson, Norb Schemansky, John Davis, Clyde Emrich, Dave Sheppard, Tommy Kono, Jim Park, Bill Pearl, George Eiferman, Mickey Hargitay, Roy (The Great) Hilligenn

. . . the 1950s, at the Varsity Club:
  Larry Choman, Lew and Bob Hart, Jim Tanzillo, Gary Neilsen, Art Plantier, Frank Montero

. . . the 1960s and 1970s, in the basement torture chamber:
  Dave Neeld, Dwight Kerr, Randy Reso, Gary Rockafellow, Bob Mason, Bert and Jim Marchio, Marshall Massa, Dave Laputka, Ed Raws, Harry Norton, Tom Ford, Jeff Neiman, Jim Feijo, Emil Pauli, Don Salvia, Joe Weider

. . . the late 1970s, at the Bucks Fitness Center:
  Mike Ludwig, Kevin Diabelko, John Savage, Kevin Gorham, Dennis and Brian Devanney, Gary Fralin, Ray Whitfield, Ken Thompson, Pat Malloy, Steve Salvatico, Scott Carrick, Ken Dierks, Doug Cauti, Mike Farley, Scott Johnston, Rick Gibney, Joe and Steve Mack, Chuck Lodge, Vince Thompson, Pat McGuffin, Bob Smith, Bob and Rich Cappiello, Bob Strandberg, Rich Banyas, Keith Beyer, Steve Bull, Walt Chekay, Rich Alpaugh, Tom Cliggett, Tom Creeden, Joe DeLago, Paul and John Kent, Bill Smith, Charlie Kohler, Craig Skuse, Harry Bozarth, John Lapent, Marty Flannery, Paul Giordano, Gary Lindenmuth, Pete Martin, Gordon and Ron May, Kyle Johnson, Shawn Passman, Don Prowant, Dick and Eric Seuring, Craig Forchetti, Tom Naudascher, Pat Tiberi, Roger Young, Adam Burghardt, Jim Di Tulio, Len Larrisey, Ron Walker, Tony LaSalle, Mark Smith, Vince Vitale, Bill Guerin, Clete Mahoney, Dave Kazanjian, Mike Riccio

. . . spanning the years:
  sons Jim and Jay; Dick Hart and his son Rich; Bill Zorichak; the human sports encyclopedia, Tom (Mr. Power Clean) Hansen

  . . . all the others who, from time to time, shared the agony of one more rep and the joy of the New Personal Record

  . . . and Jane, who cheerfully put up with it for so many years.

contents

introduction

Weight training and vigorous sports have fascinated me for more than forty years, especially sports in which measurable comparisons can be made of human performance as opposed to sports in which intangibles (pure skill, coordination) and luck (the way the ball bounces) play major roles. Upon entering our teens, several friends and I dared to lift weights in order to become stronger, mainly to play football, against our coaches' wishes. Remember, this was more than four decades ago. Our approach was haphazard, mostly consisting of seeing how much we could lift in various ways, but we still got fairly good results. Our football team won the conference championship during our last two years of high school, and we dominated local track and field competition as well.

This experience, in which we proved to ourselves that added strength improved athletic performance, cemented my interest in weight training as an important aspect of physical conditioning. At the time few people seemed to share that interest—or few were writing about it, anyway. Bob Hoffman, the publisher of *Strength & Health* magazine, often wrote that he believed weight training helped athletes in other sports, but he offered only the sketchiest hard evidence to support the contention. There were athletes who combined weight lifting with success in other athletic activities, but they were primarily wrestlers. One of the most prominent was George Hackenschmidt, a champion at both wrestling and weight lifting, who wrote an inspirational and instructive book, *The Way to Live*. Hackenschmidt was world wrestling champion from 1898 until 1911.

There were other believers in weight training, but forty years ago they were not well publicized. American sports writers, usually not especially strong or fit themselves, eulogized athletes whose primary assets were skill and coordination and gave the greatest emphasis to sports demanding these qualities. Even today such sports tend to receive the greatest attention in the media, with the exception of running, which requires little skill and is currently popular. Perhaps it's easier for most writers to identify with average-looking people and to fantasize that they, too, could field a grounder and make the throw to first if they only practiced a little. As a result, when Gottfried Wuthrich, a Swiss who immigrated to the United States, performed incredible feats of strength and endurance for the time, around the turn of the century, his achievements received little publicity. Born in 1874, Wuthrich was only 5'9¾" tall and weighed about 178 pounds in his prime, but he put the 16-pound shot 45 feet, threw the hammer 162 feet, and lifted 310 pounds overhead in the crude style of the day. And he also had the agility and endurance to perform 15,000 consecutive rope skips.

Who but a true aficionado has ever heard of Donald Dinnie, a 6', 218-pound Scotsman who, at about the time of the Civil War, put a 16-pound *stone* six inches short of 50 feet, threw a 16-pound *sledge* hammer 132 feet 8 inches, long-jumped farther than 20 feet, high-jumped 5 feet 11 inches *scissors style,* and ran 100 yards in 10.4 seconds? Dinnie trained for his track and field events by, among other things, shoving a pair of 56-pound dumbbells overhead for 52 repetitions!

Versatile, all-around athletes who trained with weights weren't confined to Europe. A contemporary of Dinnie's in the United States was William B. Curtis, a 5'8", 168-pounder who excelled in a variety of sports. Curtis ran 100 yards in 10 flat, 440 yards in 51.5; swam 100 yards in 1:40; sculled a mile in 6:49; and long-jumped more than 19 feet. Although only a lightheavyweight, Curtis hauled a pair of 100-pound dumbbells to his shoulders and rammed them overhead and also lifted 3,239 pounds clear of the ground with the aid of a harness—straps over his shoulders from which the weight was suspended.

In view of this kind of longstanding evidence, it's hard to understand how coaches in the 1940s could believe that training with weights would make a person slow and clumsy. But believe it they did, and that belief persisted into the 1950s. In 1950, while in my last year of college, and later, while working as a sports reporter, I wrote freelance articles for *Strength & Health.* I struck up a correspondence with the late Ray Van Cleef, who was then the magazine's managing editor, and urged him to report regularly on the use of weight training by outstanding athletes. By then, regardless of what the coaches kept saying, athletes had learned for themselves that weight training built useful strength. A year later, when Ray decided to open his own health club in California, he called unexpectedly to offer me the editorship of *Strength & Health* and I had the opportunity to put my own ideas into practice.

During my tenure as managing editor of *Strength & Health,* 1951–55, I formalized a "weight trained athlete of the month" feature and even departed from the standard muscle man on the cover to show such athletes as Bob Richards, a champion in the pole vault and decathlon, and Stan Jones, an All-American football player at Maryland (later an All-Pro with the Chicago Bears) posing with barbells. During those years York, Pennsylvania, was truly the hub of weight training in the United

States and I had the opportunity to train with and observe Olympic weight lifting champions, "Mr. America" and "Mr. Universe" titlists, and a constant stream of weight trained athletes, including such outstanding individuals as Richards and Jones. I also learned about the work of certain open-minded physical educators, such as C. H. McCloy of the University of Iowa, and physiologists, such as Dr. Peter V. Karpovich of Springfield College, who were studying the effects of weight training on physical performance.

The combination of these influences provided me the opportunity to write a book, *Weight Lifting and Progressive Resistance Exercise.* In it I showed Bob Richards, track and field champion; Frank Stranahan, champion golfer; and Dick Cleveland, record-setting swimmer, all training with barbells.

Two years later I had the opportunity to collaborate with Dr. Karpovich in writing *Weight Training in Athletics* (Prentice-Hall, 1956), in which he contributed a section on the physiology of exercise and I described in detail the weight training programs of champion athletes in both "major" and "minor" sports. I believe this book, carrying the highly respected byline of Peter Karpovich, had a major favorable impact on the acceptance by physical educators and coaches of weight training as a beneficial form of exercise.

Since those early years in which coaches instilled in us fears of awful "muscle-binding" and athletic ineptitude if we should lift the dreaded barbell, we have come about 180 degrees to a point where there are hundreds of strength coaches, complex and exotic weight training programs in the coaching journals, and entrepreneurs marketing all sorts of equipment to simulate or "improve on" barbells for athletic training.

This brings me, in a roundabout way, to the purpose of this book. *Winning Weight Training* represents an attempt to cut through the confusion and provide a basic, practical approach to weight training for athletic strength and physical fitness. There is, of course, much more to weight training, weight lifting, and bodybuilding than I cover in this book. If you are interested in my views on them, I suggest you read *Inside Weight Lifting and*

Weight Training (Contemporary Books, Inc., 1977) and *Inside Bodybuilding* (Contemporary Books, Inc., 1978). This book, however, will tell you as much as you need to know about how to apply weight training practically as an adjunct to skill and endurance training for sports proficiency and fitness.

The approach described in this book is distilled from more than forty years of experience and observation, which have

The author is pictured emphasizing correct straight-backed lifting position at a weight training clinic held at the Plainfield Area (New Jersey) YMCA. Son Jim Murray III demonstrates. The author played football, threw the javelin in college and AAU meets, and won medals and trophies in weight lifting. His son was a four-year varsity letterman in college football and also has competed successfully in weight lifting.

resulted in the conviction that athletes in any sport can benefit from doing the same few basic exercises. To be honest, however, I'll admit at the start that a good natural athlete will benefit from almost any of the programs and apparatus available. Working against progressively increasing resistance builds strength. And, as long as you adequately practice the skills of your sport and also develop endurance by running, the added strength will improve your performance.

winning
weight training

chapter one
winning lifelong fitness

It is possible to acquire and maintain a superior level of physical fitness through the regular practice of weight training. Any regularly practiced approach to weight training will produce more total fitness than no exercise at all, and weight training practiced for a half hour or more, with only brief rests between exercises, will produce both strength and endurance. Furthermore, weight training is the best way to increase strength and power, vital components of physical fitness.

Ideally, for the highest level of total fitness, such as that possessed by athletes who compete in the decathlon, weight training should be mixed with some form of sustained, submaximal exercise, such as running for fifteen minutes to a half hour at a speed that elevates the pulse rate to somewhere between 60 and 80 percent of its maximum rate. (A person's maximum rate is estimated by subtracting age from 220. For example, assume your age is 30. Subtract 30 from 220, which leaves 190, the likely maximum pulse rate for that age. Seventy percent of 190 is 133, so sustained exercise for a person aged 30 should be strenuous enough to maintain a pulse rate of between 115 and 150, preferably 133.)

It is possible to maintain a pulse rate in the 60 to 80 percent range while weight training simply by checking the rate between exercises or sets of an exercise and resuming exercise before the pulse drops below the 60 percent level. Exercise physiologists, who tend to be ectomorphic distance runner types, probably will contend that running, cycling, or swimming is somehow "better" for maintaining the pulse in the target range, but I find it difficult to believe that the heart knows what is causing it to beat, and I suspect the conditioning effect is about the same, regardless of the type of exercise. There is one pronounced difference, of course: if you use weight training to keep your pulse in the target range, your overall strength will be much greater than if you elevate the heart rate by running or swimming.

MIXED TRAINING

Even though I believe that many health and fitness benefits can be obtained by weight training alone, the recommended approach for an athlete seeking the benefits of this form of exercise is to use it for what it does best—building strength and power. By training with reasonably heavy weights (what is reasonable depends on your genetic makeup and athletic goal) at a leisurely pace—allowing ample recovery time between sets and exercises—you can develop strength most efficiently. And by running, or cycling, or swimming, or jumping rope separately from your weight training program, you can efficiently increase cardiorespiratory endurance without handicapping your strength routine.

Wrestling requires a combination of great skill, strength, and endurance. John Peterson, an Olympic champion, is shown here with his arm raised in victory. Peterson developed the enduring strength to power clean a 255-pound barbell for eight repetitions at a body weight of 195 pounds. *(Photo by Bruce Klemens)*

PROGRESSIVE WEIGHT TRAINING

To make the greatest gains in strength and in power, which is defined as strength with speed, you must train strenuously against progressively increasing resistance. No matter what form the resistance takes, working muscles against increasingly heavy loads will gradually build strength, providing you also allow your body rest periods to recuperate and also follow other prudent health rules, such as obtaining a nourishing, balanced diet.

Without special equipment you can strengthen arm, chest, and shoulder muscles by doing sets of eight to ten push-ups, placing a brick or some similar heavy object between your shoulder blades and adding another brick or replacing it with a heavier object whenever it becomes easy to complete three or more sets of ten push-ups. You can strengthen your legs by carrying weights, such as a small person sitting on your shoulders, up stairs. These are crude ways to train for strength, however, and a much better way is to exercise with progressively heavier barbells and dumbbells.

SPECIAL APPARATUS

It is also possible to increase strength by exercising progressively on specially designed equipment such as the selectorized weight stacks attached to handles by pulleys and chains, sometimes employing cams (Nautilus equipment, for example) or other leverage devices (Universal Gym) to increase the resistance beyond that provided by the weights in the stacks. This equipment has advantages in convenience, since all you have to do to change the resistance is move a pin from one place to another in the stack. It is also easy to use, since it is not necessary to learn how to perform the exercise. When you use a machine you must use it in the way it was designed to be used—in a certain "groove," as it were.

The disadvantage of selectorized exercise machines is that they do restrict your freedom to move. Also, they usually exercise only one body part at a time and inhibit acceleration. If all you are trying to do is strengthen and/or enlarge individual muscles, exercise machines are effective. A leg extension machine is an excellent piece of apparatus for focusing on the muscles that stabilize the knee, for example. It is more convenient to use than the "iron boot" (metal sandal) you attach to your foot, adding a dumbbell handle and individual plates to vary the resistance. But if you are trying to develop athletic power as well as strength, freely moving barbells and dumbbells allow acceleration and permit allied muscle groups to work in coordinated unison.

4

PSEUDOSCIENCE AND HUCKSTERISM

We live in an age in which scientific terms are used loosely to help sell a vast array of exercise devices and other aids to athletic performance. Unquestionably certain advances in training approaches, equipment, and nutrition have aided the progress of athletic performance. But so have selection and recruitment and the mere passing of time; expectations keep growing, and we seem to believe that a feat can be improved upon as soon as someone accomplishes it.

An interval training approach—running fast individual quarter miles with ever briefer rests between them—certainly helped Roger Bannister become the first man to run a mile in less than four minutes. But the mere fact that Bannister had done it allowed countless others to believe it could be done and follow him through that previously impassable four-minute barrier. The same is true of the 60- and then the 70-foot shot put and the 400- and then the 500-pound clean and jerk.

There are those who would ascribe this progress to a certain food supplement or type of apparatus or drug—usually the one they are selling. And they often can cite "scientific" evidence to support their beliefs. This is especially amusing to me, after having spent a quarter of a century studying and writing about medical and pharmaceutical developments as well as about physical training. During that time I've become sensitive to the wide variety of quality in scientific work and the publications devoted to science.

One thing I learned at an early stage is that a scientist can usually find what he is looking for and, even if he doesn't find it in the data, he can hedge a few carefully worded statements in his discussion and conclusion to make it seem as though he had. Years ago a scientist studied runners and found that those with the strongest arms ran fastest. He thereupon recommended that runners exercise to strengthen their arms. It probably did no harm for runners to strengthen their arms, but a better recommendation would have called for runners to train for general

Sam Walker, pictured jerking a 462-pound barbell overhead, is a prime example of a successful weight trained athlete. Walker, the first high school boy to put the 12-pound shot farther than 70 feet and an outstanding football player, went on to rank with the best in the world at putting the 16-pound shot and won U.S. weight lifting championships. *(Photo by Bruce Klemens)*

strength because the only thing the scientist really proved with his study was that strong runners are faster than weak ones.

Another study showed that similar benefits in aerobic conditioning were achieved through a half hour of jogging and fifteen minutes of rope skipping, leading to the conclusion that rope skipping was twice as effective as jogging. Jogging for fifteen minutes was not studied, however. Apparently, it never occurred to anyone that fifteen minutes might be the critical factor, after which the exercise returned diminishing rewards in aerobic conditioning changes.

Now we can find reports of studies, duly garnished with "data," to show that contracting muscles against machines is vastly superior to any other kind of old-fashioned, nonscientific training. To use an old-fashioned, nonscientific phrase, that is a lot of horsefeathers. It may be true (and I believe from personal experience that it is) that duplicating *specific* athletic skills against significantly greater resistance is of little value and quite possibly counterproductive. It does not follow, however, that powerful movements, coordinated and with acceleration, are not an effective way to develop power that is readily transferred to improved performance in other sports.

Nor does it follow that slowly contracting muscles against the resistance of a machine is the best way to develop functional strength and power for sports. Nautilus equipment is an excellent training medium for strengthening and enlarging specific, individual muscles. But to base an athletic strengthening program exclusively on Nautilus machines flies in the face of long experience, which shows that basic barbell exercises build the power to break records in every measurable kind of athletic achievement. This fact is verified every day by the best athletes in the world.

EQUIPMENT

Three pieces of equipment are essential to an effective weight training program: a heavy adjustable barbell, a pair of squat stands, and a bench with uprights to support the barbell. The best barbell is an Olympic set, but exercise sets can·also be used effectively. The Olympic bar is seven feet long and revolves smoothly. A 310-pound Olympic set costs about $320 to $350 plus freight charges. A 400-pound Olympic set costs from $375 to $400, plus freight. You could make up a serviceable exercise set, however, by purchasing a six-foot knurled (with roughened grip areas) exercise barbell with collars (about 30 pounds total weight), two 50-pound plates, four 25-pound plates, four 10-pound plates, two 5-pound plates, and two 2½-pound plates, for about $125 to $150, plus freight.

A pair of squat stands, adjustable for height, costs about $50 to $60, and a bench made for bench pressing costs about $35 to $50. All mail order equipment carries freight charges, but it still tends to be less expensive than equipment purchased at retail sporting goods stores. The advantages of retail stores, of course, are that the equipment is immediately available and you have an opportunity to examine it before buying.

Mail order sources of equipment include the York Barbell Company, Inc., PO Box 1707, York, PA 17405; Weider Health & Fitness, Inc., 21100 Erwin St., Woodland Hills, CA 91367; and Body Culture Equipment Company, 808 W. 5th, PO Box 10, Alliance, NE 69301. Addresses of other suppliers can be found in the various weight training/bodybuilding/physical culture magazines available on newsstands.

BEFORE YOU BEGIN

Before undertaking a weight training program, either to improve athletic performance or to keep fit, there are several things you should understand:

1. Building strength and power through weight training will not guarantee athletic success. You must also master the specific skills of your sport and specifically condition yourself by practicing those skills.

2. After reading the instructions you should first practice the

exercise with very light weights to be sure you understand the performance. Then you should increase the weights to amounts you can handle comfortably for three sets of ten repetitions of the exercise and stay at that level for a week (three workouts, alternating exercise and rest days). This will allow you to determine, by cautious experiment, how much weight you should use for the numbers of repetitions and sets that are recommended. (A set is one bout of a given number of repetitions. If you are doing five sets of three repetitions, or *reps,* with increasing weights, it means you take the starting weight and lift it three times. Then add weight and do three more—the second set—add weight again, three more reps, for a total of fifteen, three at a time.)

3. Before starting to exercise, if you have any doubt about your general health, get a checkup by a doctor to be sure you don't have unsuspected heart disease, hernia, or some musculo-skeletal problem that would either prohibit or limit your activity.

4. Exercising with weights is not without risk. As with any vigorous sport or exercise, it is possible to suffer injuries. Surprisingly, perhaps, weight training—when done properly—is one of the safest of physical activities, because progression can be and should be gradual. Nevertheless, when trying to set personal records, it is possible to strain or sprain muscles and/or tendons and/or ligaments. Most injuries will be minor, usually forcing you to cease or modify your training for a while at worst. The usual strain or sprain is best treated by immediately applying an ice pack and reapplying ice every half hour or when the ice melts for the first twelve hours, then by applying heat and gradually resuming activity at a level that does not cause pain. For more severe injuries, or when you're in doubt about the severity of an injury, of course you should see a physician.

5. Patience will pay big dividends. No matter how much you want to be a champion, you are more likely to become one if you progress gradually and build steadily for the future rather than try to exercise with the heaviest possible weights in the hope of becoming a world-beater in a month.

9

chapter two

the basic three for strength and power

There are three basic exercises that can form the nucleus of a training program for any athlete whose sport requires a great deal of strength and power. Football, the throwing events in track and field, and wrestling are examples of such sports. In fact, athletes in any sport could depend almost exclusively on these three exercises if they had little time to devote to strength training. The exercises are the power clean, the supine press on bench (bench press), and the parallel squat (to knee level).

THE POWER CLEAN

I've been touting the power clean for athletic conditioning for the past quarter of a century for several reasons. For one thing, it is a total body exercise. When done for several repetitions, repeated in sets with little rest between sets, it is a conditioner as well as a strengthener. It is especially effective for training the large muscles of the legs and torso to move powerfully—to exert strength quickly. And it trains an athlete to work major muscle groups in a coordinated, explosive, accelerated move that is much like the initial move in many athletic games. The powerful leg and torso extension of the power clean is like the start from a crouch in football, the vertical jump so important in basketball and volleyball, the racing start in swimming, the lifting of an opponent for a takedown in wrestling, the shot-putter's start across the circle, and the hammer thrower's lift as he provides final impetus to the ball and chain.

The reasons for selecting the bench press and squat as two of the three key basic exercises for athletic strength building are obvious, but the selection of the power clean needs explanation. I first began to recognize the usefulness of the exercise in the early 1950s. My own athletic participation was essentially over, though I was still occasionally throwing the javelin in AAU competition and was dabbling in competitive weight lifting as a member of the York Barbell Club while working as managing editor of *Strength & Health*. I also enjoyed helping with the coaching of budding young athletes. One who showed great promise was John Terpak, Jr., son of the former world middleweight weight lifting champion. John Terpak, Sr., was general manager of the York Barbell Company and kept in great shape in his early forties through very abbreviated weight training. John was coaching his son in weight lifting (young John won an AAU novice meet while still in high school) and I was helping him with shot putting.

To make a long story short, the main exercise that John gave his son to prepare for weight lifting was the power clean. But young John, though a good lifter, actually became better in football and track. He won shot put championships in high school, beating much bigger competitors, and went on to star as a halfback on the University of Pennsylvania football team. In retrospect I could see that the explosive power developed through extensive work on the power clean had laid the foundation for John Terpak's versatile athletic success.

WHAT DO CHAMPION ATHLETES PREFER?

There have been many debates on the merits of "quick" lifts such as the Olympic snatch and clean and jerk versus the "pure" strength builders used in power competition—the squat, bench press, and dead lift. Dave Davis, himself a strong lifter and world class shot-putter, asked several of the world's best field events athletes which they preferred (reported in *Track Technique,* March and June 1974, Track & Field News, Inc.). They were divided on the question. Brian Oldfield, Al Feuerbach, Bruce Wilhelm, and Sam Walker favored the quick lifts, while George Woods and Randy Matson leaned toward the strength lifts. Matson, who said his height and poor lifting leverage kept him from handling enough poundage in the Olympic lifts, thought his work on such exercises as the bench press and squat added six to seven feet to his throw. Oldfield said two years of concentrated weight training had improved his strength, "and you can't throw far without a base strength. Weight training gives you the confidence and strength to perform consistently at a higher level."

If there was any real consensus among the champion shot-putters, it was that a mixture of quick and strength lifts is effective. Feuerbach and Oldfield specifically mentioned the combination. Woods and Matson, who both did bench presses and squats, also did power cleans. And that brings us back to the combination recommended here. The power clean provides explosive exercise similar to Olympic lifting but without the necessity for learning Olympic lift form. Unless an athlete is specifically interested in competitive Olympic lifting, there is no need to master the complex technique of the snatch and clean and jerk. The power clean provides the same physical benefits in much less time.

Displaying the superb physique of a well-conditioned weight trained athlete, Al Feuerbach jerks a barbell overhead that weighs more than 400 pounds. Feuerbach, a 6'1", 240-pounder, set a world record in the shot put and won the U.S. 242-pound class weight lifting championship within a single year. *(Photo by Bruce Klemens)*

THE POWER CLEAN—HOW TO DO IT

The power clean is done as follows. Stand close to the barbell, feet spaced a comfortable distance apart (about hip width), toes pointed either straight ahead or toeing out slightly. Stand close enough that you can see your feet projecting past the barbell handle, so your shins touch or nearly touch the handle as you crouch to grasp it. You should place your hands in an overhand grip (knuckles away from you) slightly wider than the width of your shoulders. Then bend your knees and concentrate on achieving a position in which your hips are lower than your shoulders and your back is straight. (Try to arch it slightly; do *not* allow your back to round as you lift from the floor.)

Look at the accompanying illustrations. The starting position is a crouch with legs bent, arms straight but relaxed, and hips lower than shoulders. Your back is straight or slightly arched. Take your time and get it right. It often seems easier to lift incorrectly at first, but if you don't do it right from the start and keep doing it right, your progress will be limited. And your chances of pulling muscles, ligaments, and tendons in your back—a painful injury—will be much greater.

The actual lift should begin deliberately, not with a yank off the floor. Just straighten your legs so your hips and torso rise, keeping the torso inclined and maintaining a straight back. As you do this the barbell will leave the floor and rise to knee height. As the barbell handle reaches the tops of your knees, shift it back over your thighs with your arms, which should still be hanging straight. As the barbell reaches mid-thigh height, accelerate the extension of your legs and back and pull upward—*hard*—by shrugging your shoulders and pulling with your arms. At the height of the pull your hips will be forward, you will be leaning slightly backward, your legs will be straight, and you will have risen quickly on your toes (it *will* happen without your thinking about it) as the barbell rises in front of your abdomen to chest height.

At the height of the pull you should bend your knees again, turn your hands over, and thrust your elbows forward, catching

Jim Murray III shows perfect starting position for the power clean: legs bent, hips lower than shoulders, back flat, and arms hanging straight. He has power cleaned 255 pounds while weighing 180.

This photo shows the position at which you should explode with acceleration in the power clean. With legs still bent, the lifter is about to extend fully, shrug his shoulders upward, and pull with his arms.

This photo was snapped a split second after the lifter reached full leg and back extension in the power clean. Note that he is still up on his toes and pulling with his arms, but his knees are beginning to bend again.

After completing the total body effort—leg and back extension and hard pull with the arms—the lifter bends his knees and turns the barbell over, beginning to thrust his elbows forward under the weight as he receives it at his chest.

Completion of the power clean, with the barbell held securely across the front of the shoulders.

19

the barbell across your upper chest and the fronts of your shoulders. The final knee bend allows your knees to act as shock absorbers as you catch the barbell.

Stand erect a moment, holding the weight, then lower it to your thighs, again bending your knees for control. You can perform repetition cleans from a point at mid-thigh or from approximately knee height, or from the floor. Remember to maintain a straight back while you lower the weight as well as while you lift it.

A couple of details: As you complete the pull upward with a heavy weight, you may find that you'll naturally jump and spread your feet apart as you bend your knees to receive the weight at your chest. That's all right. It seems to be a natural movement for most of the good athletes I've seen do power cleans. Also, it will help you hold on to the barbell if you use a "hook" grip, which simply means that you wrap your thumb around the bar and the first or first and second fingers wrap around *over* the thumb.

The power clean is an exercise that produces good benefits without the use of extremely heavy weights, but as with all weight training exercises, the benefits are greater as the weights lifted get heavier—assuming the exercise is performed properly. About half of your body weight is a good amount to experiment with in the power clean, though it is prudent to begin with even less weight.

An Olympic barbell with the largest standard plates (heavier plates are available for serious competitors) weighs 132 pounds if a kilo set is used and 135 pounds if the weights are listed in pounds. (With a kilo set, the bar and the large standard plates each weigh 20 kilos—44 pounds—for a total of 60 kilos or 132 pounds. One kilo is 2.2 pounds. The bar and large standard plates in a set graduated in pounds each weigh 45, for a total of 135.) So, to gain the favorable starting position that can be achieved when the barbell is highest off the floor, it is necessary to exercise with 132 or 135 pounds. Obviously, this is too much for most people to begin with, but it is achievable by most men and the stronger women and is a heavy enough weight to give all but the strongest athletes a good workout. [A good goal for an athlete is to do five repetitions in the power clean with from 20 to 40 pounds less than body weight, three repetitions with 10 to 20 pounds less than body weight, and a single power clean with body weight to body weight plus 10 or 20 pounds.]

Most of the good young football players, shot-putters, and wrestlers I've worked with over the years have become strong enough to power clean at least their body weight. One good collegiate wrestler who was a strong bench presser reached a level where he could clean about 20 to 30 pounds more than he weighed. A football player who was a starting guard at a medium-sized college power cleaned 10 pounds more than his 205-pound body weight and 5 pounds more than he could bench press. This suggests that a body weight power clean may be a better indicator of athletic ability than a heavy bench press.

Jon Kolb, a mainstay of the Pittsburgh Steelers' Super Bowl championship teams at offensive tackle, is pictured warming up with some easy power cleans. Kolb, a 6'3", 270-pounder, is one of the strongest men in football with bench presses of 500-plus to his credit. In one televised "strongman" contest, Kolb won the "cheat curl" contest by completing twenty-two repetitions with 250 pounds in a lift done much like an underhand clean from the thighs. The powerful Kolb also bench pressed 350 pounds for eleven repetitions and squatted just short of parallel for twenty-three repetitions with 550 pounds. *(Photo courtesy of Pittsburgh Steelers)*

21

A number of national and world class athletes have worked up to very heavy weights in the power clean. An example of incredible power and endurance is the eight repetitions that Olympic wrestling champion John Peterson, at a body weight of 195 pounds, could perform with a 255-pound barbell. Many leading shot-putters, hammer throwers, discus throwers, and football players—themselves weighing 250 pounds or more—power clean more than 300 pounds. Dick Hart, who made the NFL all-rookie team during his first year and was a starting guard with the Philadelphia Eagles for several years, could power clean more than 300 pounds during off-season workouts at a weight of 255. As a 240-pound high school senior, Dick set a Pennsylvania state high school shot put record that stood for twenty years, and at the time he could power clean 275 pounds without actually trying his limit in the lift. He cleaned the 275 to press it.

How strong should a woman athlete be in the power clean? It will be difficult for women to clean as much as men, because upper body strength, as well as the legs and back, are involved in the exercise. And, of course, women lack the male hormone in the quantities needed to build strength comparable to that of a strong man. Well-coordinated athletic women can clean heavy weights, however. One outstanding example is Jan Svendsen, a leading discus thrower (180 feet 11 inches) and shot-putter (53 feet 5½ inches), ranking in the all-time top ten American women in both events as this book was written. About 6 feet tall and a nicely proportioned 172 pounds, Svendsen had a personal record of 205 pounds in the power clean.

THE BENCH PRESS

The most effective single exercise for developing the major upper body muscles—arms, shoulders, and chest—is the supine press on bench. The reason the exercise is effective is that it brings so many muscles into play in concert that relatively heavy weights can be used. The greater the resistance that is overcome, the more strength that is developed.

To practice the bench press you need, in addition to a barbell, a sturdy bench about ten inches wide, forty-eight inches long, and eighteen inches high. It should be a bench specifically designed for the exercise, with uprights to place the barbell on when you are not actually lifting it. You can, however, use a bench without uprights if you have a pair of adjustable squat stands, which can be set at various heights from about thirty-five to fifty-six inches.

With the barbell in place on uprights at the head end of the bench, you should lie on the bench with your feet on the floor and reach up to space your hands evenly on the barbell handle, somewhat wider than shoulder width. An intermediate spacing is best for all-around muscle strengthening. This is a grip wide enough so that, as you push the barbell upward from your chest, your forearms are in a vertical position. The wider the grip, the more your chest muscles provide the major impetus; the narrower the grip, the more your arm muscles are involved. Your shoulders, especially the front part of the deltoid muscles, are involved regardless of your hand spacing.

Although the intermediate grip produces the best all-around results, it is a good idea occasionally to perform some bench presses with exaggeratedly wide and narrow hand spacing. Discus throwers, in particular, will benefit from pressing with a wide grip, keeping elbows out to the side throughout the exercise.

Performance is simple. Lift the barbell off the supports, take a full breath and lower it to touch your chest across the lower part of the chest muscles, and immediately push (press) it back up to the straight-arm position. Some instructors recommend that you exhale as you straighten your arms, but I do not believe you can exert force effectively if your chest is moving. I think you should inhale, lower and press the weight, then exhale (or take several breaths), inhale and repeat.

When bench pressing, you should never attempt a weight you are not absolutely certain you can lift unless you have someone standing by as a spotter to help if you cannot straighten your arms. This includes not only attempts at setting a personal record with a single lift but also attempts to do an extra repetition

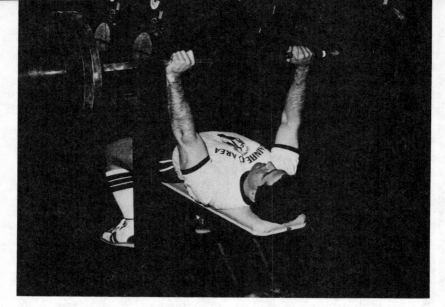

Ideal starting and finishing position for the bench press is demonstrated by Bert Marchio, three-time winner of the New Jersey state power lifting championship in the 181-pound class. A former high school football player (guard and linebacker), Bert began concentrating on power lifting in college, has an official 350-pound bench press and an unofficial best of 380 pounds, with a pause at the chest.

In the bench press, the barbell is lowered to touch across the bottom of the chest muscles, as Bert Marchio demonstrates with an easy 275 pounds, and then is pushed immediately back to the straight-arm position.

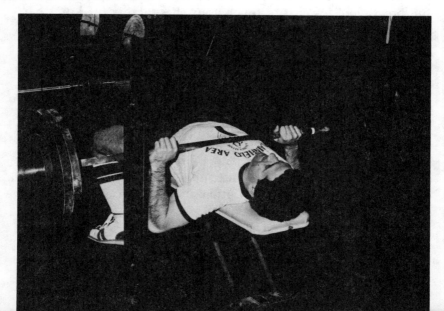

you are not certain you can complete. Usually it is possible to struggle out after being pinned by a barbell, but it is no fun and can be dangerous if really heavy weights are used.

How much should you be able to bench press in order to be a successful athlete? To some extent it depends on your sport. Shot-putters and football players need more strength than tennis players and distance runners. I've known mediocre athletes who could bench press very heavy weights and good football players who couldn't bench press barbells much heavier than their own body weights, however, so it's very difficult to generalize.

Although many authorities on weight training insist that an athlete should do more, I suspect that bench pressing body weight or 10 to 20 pounds more is a good primary goal, especially for a high school athlete. A better goal for athletes in sports that demand a lot of strength and/or protective muscle around the upper body is to bench press body weight plus 50 pounds. Sufficient strength to bench press body weight plus 100 pounds is certainly an asset to shot-putters, discus throwers, and football linemen. But even in sports demanding great strength and power, sheer strength as measured by the bench press is not the whole answer. For example, Randy Matson clearly established himself as an all-time great shot-putter when he became the first to put the 16-pound shot past 70 feet, but a lot of shot-putters who trailed him by 5 feet or more in the event could outlift him by 50 to 100 pounds in the bench press.

Matson was very tall, and his long arms provided an advantage in applying force to the shot, but put him at a disadvantage in pressing heavy barbells. When he first broke the 70-foot barrier, his best bench press was reported to be 360 pounds. Later in his career Matson became stronger and put the shot farther. For him, however, a 360-pound bench press—combined with great athletic coordination, quickness, leverage, competitive spirit, and good form—represented enough strength to make him the dominant shot-putter in the world. Others, not as tall, quick, and well-coordinated as Matson, have required much more strength to put the shot as far as Matson.

WHEN IS AN ATHLETE STRONG ENOUGH?

The point I'm trying to make is that an athlete should strive to develop strength and power with weight training but should realize that at some point he or she is strong enough. When a man becomes strong enough to bench press 250–300 pounds, he is strong enough to be an effective football player, though he obviously has an added advantage if he can become stronger. Once he gets into that "strong enough" range, however, other elements of his athletic preparation may become more significant than acquiring more strength—elements such as moving more quickly and skillfully, for example.

As an indication of what various outstanding athletes have been able to lift in the bench press, consider the following examples: Dave Wottle, former Olympic 800-meter champion, was very strong for a slender middle-distance runner, bench pressing 180 pounds while weighing only 140. Another runner, sprinter Harvey Glance, was reported to have bench pressed 300 pounds while weighing just under 150. A world class sprinter who covered 100 meters in 10.14 seconds, Glance had great power and superb muscular development at 5'7½". Wottle, whose event required more endurance and therefore emphasized sustained running that tends to handicap power, also had poorer pressing leverage, being more than 4 inches taller as well as lighter than the sprinter.

Wrestling requires a combination of strength and endurance. One of the strongest wrestlers, pound for pound, was former national collegiate champion Don Rohn, who won the title at 134 pounds while representing Clarion State College of Pennsylvania. Only a couple of inches over five feet in height, the muscular Rohn bench pressed 325 pounds!

An instructive contrast in approaches to the bench press is seen by comparing the training programs of slender distance running star Craig Virgin and the ageless master of the discus, Al Oerter. Virgin, a slim 5'10" and 138 pounds, of necessity concentrated his athletic training on running an average of eighty miles a week. He would run, for example, four miles in

26

Bench pressing with an exaggeratedly wide grip, such as that demonstrated by Vince Thompson in the illustrations, puts added stress on the chest and front of the shoulders, making it a useful variation on the exercise for discus throwers.

the morning and another eight to ten miles in the evening. In addition, however, he would work out with weights three times a week whenever weight training facilities were available to him. In the bench press Craig Virgin simply used 100 pounds and did as many repetitions as possible. Oerter, a massive 6'4" and 260 pounds, won the first of four Olympic gold medals in the discus throw in 1956. In 1980, when he was past 40 years of age, Oerter had the second best throw in the world at 227 feet 11 inches. Always one of the strongest men in the field events, Oerter had a best single in the bench press of 500 pounds and could squat with 600 pounds.

Bench pressing with hands close together, as illustrated, focuses on the triceps muscles, which extend the arms. This variation is helpful to shot-putters and javelin throwers.

WOMEN ATHLETES WHO ARE STRONG BENCH PRESSERS

Although it is unusual for a woman, even a good athlete, to be able to bench press a barbell equal to body weight, several have reached impressive poundages. Especially noteworthy is Jane Frederick, a 5'11", 157-pound pentathlon champion who currently ranks as America's all-time best in the event. Some of Frederick's best performances included a 5-foot 11-inch high jump, a 21-foot 6¼-inch long jump, a 2:14.6 time for the 800-meter run, a time of 13.25 in the 100-meter hurdles, and a 53-foot 1-inch shot put.

When the women's multi-event track and field competition was increased by two events to become a heptathlon, Jane Frederick promptly established herself as America's best in that athletic test as well. In the two added events, she ran 200 meters in 24.92 seconds and threw the javelin 154 feet. Frederick also had a personal record of 205 pounds in the bench press, a remarkable effort for a tall, trim woman training on a variety of events.

Another woman who developed almost unbelievable prowess in the bench press is Beverly Francis, winner of the 181-pound weight class in the women's world power lifting championship (squat, bench press, and dead lift) in 1981. As a power lifting specialist, she wouldn't be a candidate for mention in this book, but Bev Francis was also a leading Australian shot-putter with a distance of 55 feet to her credit. She proved the exception to the rule that women lack upper body strength by bench pressing an amazing 330 pounds! Her lift, made at a height of 5'5", when she weighed under the 181-pound class limit, would be an excellent effort for a man. As this book was written, Francis was the only woman ever to have been credited with a bench press of 300 pounds.

It is also noteworthy that Francis's 20-pound edge in body weight and 125-pound advantage in the bench press translated to only a two-foot better shot put than that recorded by Frederick, who was not a shot putting specialist. As was pointed out earlier, sheer strength is not the whole story of success in athletics, even in events requiring strength and power. Another example of this is Lorna Griffin, a 5'11", 178-pound athlete who set an American record of 207 feet 5 inches in the discus throw and also put the shot 53 feet 10½ inches. Like Francis, Lorna Griffin competed successfully in power lifting, winning the U.S. women's 181-pound class championship in 1980. Her bench press in the contest was 209 pounds, a fine effort for a tall, trim female athlete excelling in two sports. Although she did not bench press as much as Francis, Griffin credited increased strength from weight training with substantial increases in her discus throw, moving her up to the 180- to 200-foot range. Obviously, she had also mastered the technique of the event.

WHEN ENOUGH IS ENOUGH!

My belief that at some point an athlete becomes strong enough to perform well at his chosen sport is shared by a number of knowledgeable strength coaches for professional football teams. Polled by Bill Kumagai, of *Power & Fitness* magazine, here's what some of them had to say.

> The fact that one player can lift more does not necessarily make him better than a player who lifts less. There are many variables to consider.
>
> —Bob Mischak, Oakland Raiders

> You can't be prejudicial about a player just because he can't meet certain numbers. The bottom line is how well he performs on the field.
>
> —Kim Woods, Cincinnati Bengals

> Some people are not physiologically suited to bench pressing, so why embarrass them? The name of the game is still football.
>
> —Clyde Emrich, Chicago Bears

Clyde Emrich, with a background as one of the world's best competitive weight lifters during the 1950s, recommends basic barbell exercises for the areas of the body he calls the *power zones*—the legs, back, and shoulders. Among the key exercises he prescribes are squats, power cleans, bench presses, standing presses, leg presses, pulls (like unfinished power cleans), and dead lifts. The Bears' star running back, Walter Payton, power cleaned 250 pounds at a body weight of 205, without extending himself, and bench pressed more than 300 pounds. Emrich made the following eminently sensible comment to Bill Kumagai: "A person is a good football player because of inherited characteristics. Weight training is a magnifier of ability, but the ability has to be there."

Other leading strength coaches hold similar views, according to Kumagai. Les Steckel of the Minnesota Vikings recommends bench presses, squats, power cleans, and leg presses, commenting that exercise with free weights takes "more coordination and balance and adds athletic ability."

Bob Ward of the Dallas Cowboys concurs: "We look at the basic fitness factor involved in the performance of various football tasks. These vary a bit according to position, but they all draw from the same well. In terms of power, there are only so many exercises you can do, and these are free weight exercises. You can use machines also, but they don't work as well for power as free weights." An example of a great natural athlete who benefited from a basic approach, Randy White, the Cowboys' outstanding defensive tackle, has bench pressed 475 pounds and power cleaned 350.

THE SQUAT

Just as the bench press is the single most effective exercise for the upper body, the squat with barbell on shoulders is the most effective exercise for the legs and hips. It is also a good all-around strengthener, having a positive effect on torso strength as well as on leg strength.

To perform squats with enough weight to do justice to the large, powerful leg muscles, you will need squat stands to get the barbell into position. Those with adjustable height are the most practical, since people of different sizes can use them comfortably with a simple adjustment that takes only a few seconds. The stands should be set at a height that allows you to take the weight across the back of your shoulders with only a slight bend of your knees (about a one-eighth bend).

With the barbell resting on the supports, place your hands considerably farther apart than the width of your shoulders and duck under the bar, coming back up so that its center hits the center line of your body but holding it low enough so the bar is padded by the muscles of your upper back and does not press on your spine at the base of your neck. Keeping your back straight or slightly arched, as when lifting from the floor, straighten your legs to clear the barbell from the supports and back away with short steps until you are about three to five feet from the stands.

At a weight training clinic at the Plainfield Area (New Jersey) YMCA, the author calls the attention of an audience to the low position of the barbell across the back of the shoulders for squatting. Carrying the weight low, as shown, improves lifting leverage and keeps pressure from the barbell away from the spinal column at the neck.

Bert Marchio demonstrates the squat with 275 pounds, which is a very light weight for him. His best was 600 pounds as this book went to press. Note that he maintains a straight back throughout, leaning forward in the low position, and that he goes just low enough for the tops of his thighs to be parallel with the floor.

Set your feet comfortably apart—hip width or slightly wider—with toes pointed straight ahead or turned outward a little. Take a full breath, high in your chest and, maintaining a position with chest high, waist in, back straight or arched, bend your knees until your hips are at approximately knee level. This is a point at which the tops of your thighs would be parallel to the floor. Rise immediately, exhale, and repeat. In doing several repetitions, you will need to take several breaths between squats.

After completing the number of squats you planned to do, step forward and carefully replace the barbell on the stands. Look at one side and then the other to be sure it is in the right place before you relax and duck out from under the barbell. As with bench pressing, never attempt a limit effort or a repetition you aren't absolutely sure you can complete unless you have a spotter—preferably two.

In practicing squats as a conditioning exercise, there is no need to go any deeper than parallel. There has been some controversy about the effect of deep (all the way down) squats on the knee joint. Some physiologists contend that deep squats damage the joint. Other trainers with extensive experience in weight training insist that deep squats do no harm. From my own observations over forty years, I doubt that deep squats themselves damage the knees. I believe they stretch the supporting structures, however, and may make the knee more vulnerable to injury in sports where multidirectional, random forces are applied.

Since there is no need to go deeper than a parallel bend when practicing squats as a conditioning exercise, it seems a reasonable precaution to stop at that level. One way to control depth is to squat while standing in front of an exercise bench, sinking only low enough to touch the bench. A standard exercise bench is eighteen inches high, so unless you are quite short, the distance between the floor and the popliteal space at the back of your knee (at the top of the calf muscle) where your leg bends is probably greater than eighteen inches.

It is possible to handle very heavy weights in squats. Some of the football linemen and the large, strong, well-coordinated athletes specializing in the shot put, hammer throw, and discus perform repetition squats with 400, 500, and even 600 pounds. At the start, however, it is advisable to err on the conservative side and experiment with weights of about half body weight. A weight should be selected, by experiment, that will permit the first one-third to one-half the number of repetitions to be completed easily, with only the final third being really difficult. For example, suppose you are starting out with a progressive program in which you are going to do ten repetitions. The first four should be quite easy, the next three should require substantial effort, and the final three should make you really put out.

How much weight should you strive for as a goal? A football lineman should try to work up until he can squat a few repetitions with a barbell equal in weight to the weight of the largest men he will have to face. That will provide both the functional strength to get the job done and the confidence to know it is possible to do so!

It is always comforting to have more than enough strength than just an adequate amount. Therefore, most athletes in "heavy" sports (football, weight throwing events, wrestling) tend to work up to training weights that rival the poundages used by competitive weight lifters. If your largest opponent is likely to

One of the strongest men and best offensive centers in football, Mike Webster is pictured performing repetition squats with 315 pounds in the Pittsburgh Steelers weight room. A key member of the Steelers' Super Bowl teams, the 6'1", 265-pound Webster won two events and the overall contest in the televised "strongest man in football" competition. Webster bench pressed 350 pounds for fifteen repetitions and squatted to a near-parallel level twenty-five times with 550 pounds. *(Photo courtesy of Pittsburgh Steelers)*

weigh 250 pounds, extra confidence and superior performance come with the knowledge that your legs are strong enough to extend five times against a resistance of 300 pounds, or 350, or 400.

Sooner or later, however, you reach a level where additional strength is superfluous and you would be spending your time more productively with a program that maintains strength while you work on total conditioning and finely honing your skills. That point arrives much earlier when preparing for "light" sports (baseball, basketball, tennis) than for "heavy" ones. As an indication of how strong some leading football players are, Mike Webster, center for the Pittsburgh Steelers' Super Bowl championship team, completed twenty-five repetition squats with a 550-pound barbell on his shoulders, with each squat done to a depth slightly short of parallel. Webster weighed 267 pounds at a height of 6'1". His teammate, Jon Kolb, an offensive tackle, squatted twenty-three repetitions with the same weight at a body weight of 273. And Robert Young, an outstanding guard with the Chicago Cardinals and later with the Houston Oilers, squatted twenty-two times with 550 pounds at a body weight of 286. All three men were undoubtedly capable of more, since they performed their squats in a contest among professional football players after having already extended themselves in two other all-out tests of strength.

WOMEN'S LEG STRENGTH

Women are at less disadvantage by comparison with men in tests of leg strength than in tests of upper body and whole body strength. Three of the women track and field athletes mentioned previously—Jan Svendsen, Lorna Griffin, and Beverly Francis—squatted with heavy weights in official power lift contests. Jan Svendsen squatted with approximately 100 pounds more than her weight, succeeding with 275 pounds; Lorna Griffin squatted with 374; and powerful Bev Francis squatted with 473. The latter weight, in particular, would be a good effort for a male

It is prudent to have spotters standing by when bench pressing and squatting. To limit the depth of a squat, it's also a good idea to stand in front of a knee-high bench and just squat deep enough to touch it. Demonstrating is Stacey Thompson, a 5'7", 125-pound runner who competes in the 100- and 200-meter dashes, the 400-meter relay, and the mile relay for Wilson High School in Bucks County, Pennsylvania. The spotters are Nancy Borden, left, her track coach, and teammate Beatrice Webb, right. Nancy, a runner as well as a coach, has completed several full marathons. Bea, a 5', 110-pound speedster, competes in the same events as Stacey and also runs 400 meters. Bea has bench pressed 140 pounds.

athlete not specializing in weight lifting, as would her 330-pound bench press and 462-pound dead lift. In fact, those would be good lifts for football players weighing more than 200 pounds! Francis, incidentally, also was credited with a clean and jerk of 231 pounds (at a 162-pound body weight) and an 11.5-second time for running 100 meters. She credited weight training with increasing her sprinting speed, according to a report that appeared in *Iron Man* magazine.

THE LEG PRESS

Another effective exercise for developing the muscles of the thighs is the leg press, in which you sit or lie with your back braced against a support or the floor and push with your feet against pedals or a sliding platform. On a leg press machine with pedals, the weight is usually provided by a weight stack that can be varied by moving a selector pin. The sliding platform type is loaded with barbell plates.

The leg press does permit the use of heavy weights and is effective for strengthening the thighs; it is also easy to perform and requires no instruction. However, the leg press also immobilizes the back and hips, and thus fails to develop all the big leg, hip, and back muscles in coordinated unison.

chapter three
planning an effective program

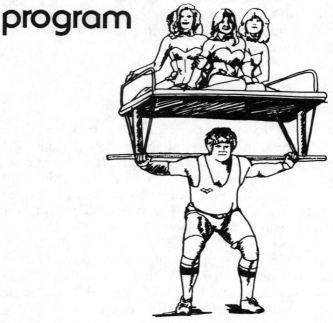

Once you have mastered correct performance of weight training exercises that build strength for athletic sports (or simply for superior physical fitness) you should plan to use them effectively. For the shot-putter or football player, that means working with heavy weights in sets of relatively low repetitions. For the wrestler, it means working with the heaviest possible weights in sets of higher repetitions to develop enduring strength. For the ball player—any ball game—it means working with light to moderate weights in sets of higher repetitions, except that basketball players will benefit from power cleans in sets of low repetitions with as much weight as they can handle in correct form.

Suppose, for example, a shot-putter, a wrestler, and a basket-ball player were going to practice the same three basic exercises for building athletic strength and power during the off-season. Here's how they might do them:

	Shot-Putter	Wrestler	Basketball Player
Power Clean	60% × 5	60% × 10	50% × 5
	70% × 5	70% × 8	60% × 5
	75% × 5	75% × 8 + 8 + 8	75% × 3
	80% × 3		80% × 3
	85% × 2 or 3		85% × 3 + 3
	90% × 1 or 2		
Bench Press	50% × 10	60% × 10	50% × 10
	70% × 5	70% × 10	65% × 10
	80% × 5	75% × 8 + 8 + 8	75% × 5–8
	90% × 3		
	95% × 1, 2, or 3		
Squat	50% × 10	50% × 10	50% × 10
	70% × 10	65% × 10	70% × 5
	80% × 5	75% × 10 + 10 + 10	75% × 5
	85% × 5 + 5 + 5		80% × 5

The foregoing percentages are based on what the athlete could lift in the exercise one time, with a limit or near-limit effort. For example, if the shot-putter could power clean 220 pounds once, as a limit, he would begin by cleaning 135 pounds as a warm-up and move up to 155, 165, 175, and finally 185 and 200 for the two sets done in the least number of repetitions.

The percentages are kept lower for the wrestler, who should be doing more repetitions for a combination of strength and endurance. Suppose the wrestler's best single bench press is 200 pounds. He would warm up with 120 for ten, move up to 140 for eight, and then grind out three sets of eight bench presses with 150.

The basketball player's approach would develop power with low repetitions in the clean and squat. It would also include enough bench pressing to develop upper body strength that is useful in rebounding.

Please note that the sets, repetitions, and percentages given here are not engraved in stone. They are intended as guidelines for the approaches to be used for different sports. In practice, most good athletes find individual approaches that they like and that bring them good results. The general technique is to start with a weight that is easy for the first set, which serves as a warm-up. The second and third sets also serve as warm-ups as you move the weight up, preparing you for the greater efforts of the final set or sets.

During off-season training, initially it is a good idea to work up to a single limit effort in each lift once a week, on different days. You might try to improve your personal record in the power clean on Monday, in the bench press on Wednesday, and in the squat on Friday.

THE CYCLE SYSTEM

Obviously, you can't keep improving on your best, week after week. When you first undertake weight training, especially if you start in your teens, it may seem possible to improve steadily for as long as four months. If your progression is interrupted by a competitive athletic season, during which you should either discontinue or reduce your weight training program to a maintenance level (70 percent of your best is plenty to work with for maintenance), you may continue to move up steadily between seasons. I had that experience myself as a high school athlete, building strength for football during summer vacation and for track during the winter after football season. Many young men I've worked with who were active in two separate sports had the same experience. But if you are specializing in one sport, or if you have reached a mature level of strength, you will need to learn how to cycle your workouts.

Cycling is the only way to avoid going stale—reaching a plateau beyond which you cannot progress. You may even fall off in your strength achievements. Even teenagers have off days in which they cannot match their previous best. The same advice applies to them: when you reach a peak and can't match it in a week's time, it is time to try the cycling approach.

The following, in tabular form, is an example of a cycling approach that works. Each workout should begin with three progressively heavier sets of the exercise, using less weight than the training weight for the day, as a warm-up.

Week One

Workout 1: 50% × 5
                55% × 5
                60% × 5
                70% × 3–5 reps × 4 sets

Workout 2: 50%, 55%, 60% × 5 each
                75% × 3–5 reps × 4 sets

Workout 3: 50%, 55%, 60% × 5 each
                70% × 3–5 reps × 4 sets

Week Two

Workout 1: 50%, 65%, 75% × 5 each
                85% × 3–5 reps × 4 sets

Workout 2: 50%, 55%, 60% × 5 each
                70% × 3–5 reps × 4 sets

Workout 3: 50%, 60%, 65% × 5 each
                80% × 3–5 reps × 4 sets

Week Three

Workout 1: 60% × 5 reps
                70% × 3 reps and 80% × 3 reps
                92% × 3 reps × 4 sets

Workout 2: 50%, 55%, 60% × 5 each
                75% × 3 reps × 4 sets

Workout 3: 50%, 60%, 65% × 5 each
                80% × 3 reps × 4 sets

Week Four

Workout 1:   50% × 5
            60% × 5
            75% × 3
            85% × 1
            95% × 1
            105% × 1 (new limit)

Workout 2:   50%, 55%, 60% × 5 each
            70% × 3 × 4 sets

Workout 3:   50% × 5
            60% × 5
            70% × 3
            80% × 1
            90% × 1
            100% × 1 (old limit)

After completing the four-week cycle, recompute the weights on the basis of your first workout of the fourth week, when presumably you will have reached 105 percent, which now becomes your new 100 percent figure. Remember, the final workout of the four-week sequence is 100 percent of the starting poundage, not the new 105 percent limit.

A strong, mature athlete will have many failures at 105 percent. In these cases, simply repeat the cycle. Remember, unless you are actually a competitive weight lifter or power lifter, the amount you can lift isn't *the* critical factor in your sport. The best bench presser isn't always the best shot-putter or football player. At some point in your strength training, you are strong enough to compete successfully. At that point it becomes important to maintain strength while striving to improve other aspects of your athletic preparation. But, in your efforts to develop all the alterable elements that contribute to athletic success—skill, strength, general condition, adequate rest, proper nutrition—a cycled approach to strength training will produce better long-term improvement than frequent attempts to better personal records.

CHAMPION ATHLETE PROGRAMS

A number of champion athletes of different physical types and with quite diverse athletic specialities have used the power clean/bench press/squat series of exercises as the mainstay of strength and power programs. Some examples that illustrate the variety of possible approaches follow.

George Woods, Champion Shot-Putter

A 6'2", 290-pound athlete agile enough to perform back flips, George Woods established a world indoor shot put record of 72 feet 2¾ inches in 1974. He warmed up by performing the exercise with a light weight and then did five sets of three to five repetitions in the bench press, working up to 390 pounds for repetitions. His best single bench press was 480. After a light warm-up he performed four sets of three to five squats, working up to 520 pounds for repetitions. His best single squat was 635. Woods worked up in the power clean in the same manner, doing four sets of three to five cleans with as much as 300 pounds for repetitions. His best single power clean was 370.

Ken Stadel, World Class Discus Thrower

Ken Standel, a 6'6", 270-pound athlete, had a personal best of 227 feet 3 inches in the discus throw. His workout was of a type favored by many athletes in sports demanding strength. First he would run a half mile. Then he would do seven sets of bench presses and power cleans, adding weight and reducing the repetitions with each set until he reached a maximum for the day. In the squat he did five sets of ten repetitions, squatting to an approximately parallel position.

Earl Bell, Pole Vaulter

Earl Bell, a rangy, muscular 6'3", 170-pound pole vaulter, mixed weight training and running to train for an 18-foot 7¼-inch vault. His runs were 330, 220, and 110 yards, and he ran those distances fast, covering 220 yards in about twenty-four seconds. With the weights, after a warm-up, he performed three sets of six bench presses with 200 pounds, three sets of six cleans with 180, and three sets of ten squats, increasing the weight from 200 to 450 pounds (and probably not going as deep as parallel).

Tommy Haynes, Jumper and Sprinter

Tommy Haynes, a 5'9", 165-pounder who excelled in the long jump (26 feet 8½ inches), triple jump (56 feet 5¼ inches), and 100-yard dash (9.6 seconds), did not practice power cleans, but his approach to the bench press and squat should be instructive to jumpers and sprinters. Haynes would perform five sets of four repetitions in the bench press, after a warm-up, and followed a gradual build-up approach in which his first workouts after a layoff would be done with 165 pounds and his final poundage a few weeks later would be an impressive 250—almost 100 pounds more than his weight. In the squat Haynes handled 200 pounds in early workouts and gradually built up to sets with 400 pounds! His workout also included a one-mile jog, running the stadium steps, 300-yard runs, and an 880 jog.

Kentucky State University Basketball Team

Kentucky State University's highly successful basketball team, coached by Silas McKinnie, followed a weight training program that stressed the power clean, bench press, and squat. They used more repetitions (ten) in the power clean than I would recommend, but they obtained excellent results, which shows that a lot of variations in approach will work if you have good raw material to start with. According to Dan Hill, strength consultant, and Jim Donlon, Kentucky State's strength coach, Patrick Mitchell—a 6'2", 180-pound guard—power cleaned 242½ pounds, and Clifford Howard—a 6'5", 220-pound forward— power cleaned 275½ pounds. In my book, those lifts rate as outstanding performances by two athletes whose sport calls primarily for skill, quickness, speed, coordination, and endurance. Can you imagine the authority with which a man as strong as Howard would jump up and grab a rebound?!

The complete program used by the Kentucky State team, as reported in *Strength & Health,* was as follows:

Power Clean: 3 sets of 10 repetitions
Bench Press: 3 sets of 10 repetitions
Half-Squat: 5 sets of 10 repetitions
Step-Up on a Bench: 3 sets of 20 step-ups
Reverse Curl: 5 sets of 12 repetitions
Sit-Up: 5 sets of 20 repetitions

As reported in *Muscle & Fitness* magazine, Jim Chones, 6'11", 225-pound forward for the championship Los Angeles Lakers pro basketball team, practiced both squats and bench presses. Pictures accompanying the article showed Chones working out at Gold's Gym, a weight training center, performing presses on an inclined bench, squats, and dumbbell curls.

Weight Training and Baseball

There is little specific information available on the actual weight training exercises practiced by major league baseball players. In a July 18, 1977, article on one of baseball's best batters, Rod Carew of the California Angels, *Time* magazine reported: "Carew has the wrists and forearms of a heavyweight, the result of a regular routine of weight lifting. He keeps a dumbbell in his locker in the clubhouse; on the field before games, he curls a thirteen-pound metal bar habitually, almost absentmindedly." Carew had a .343 batting average during the decade 1970 through 1980.

All-Star catcher Brian Downing, another member of the California Angels, also lifts weights. In an article published in *Strength & Health,* writer John Creer quoted Downing as saying, "Weights might not be for everyone, but before I was using them, I was hitting for a .220 average. Now I'm at .320."

Photos printed with the article showed Downing performing curls with a barbell that appeared to be loaded to about 75 pounds and bench presses with an Olympic barbell loaded to more than 200 pounds. The article also quoted Downing as saying he worked with weights four days a week in the off-season, doing exercises for his entire body: shoulders, biceps, triceps, chest, back, legs, and abdominal muscles.

The most extensive personal experience I've had with a baseball player involved a man who signed a bonus contract with the Braves and who reached the AAA level before he left baseball. Dick Hart performed the amazing feat of setting a Pennsylvania state shot put record as a high school senior while playing catcher well enough to be signed to a bonus contract when he graduated. Dick averaged 21 home runs a year and had 117 runs batted in while playing with Boise, Idaho, in the Pioneer League. He had given himself four years to make the Braves' regular club and, though he showed every likelihood of making it later, he stuck to his timetable and switched to pro football. So superior an athlete was he that he earned a spot with the Philadelphia Eagles as a guard—a position he had never played—without benefit of college experience. Before the season during which he attracted the attention of major league scouts, Hart was training on heavy power cleans, presses, squats, and bench presses.

The Basic Three by a Canadian Superman

Bishop Dolegiewicz, a world class shot-putter and discus thrower, illustrates the great amount of athletic strength that can be developed by the power clean, bench press, and squat approach. A Canadian, Dolegiewicz officially had put the shot 68 feet 5 inches and had thrown the discus 214 feet 5 inches as this book was being written. Unofficially he had put the shot 71 feet, so it appeared he had not yet reached his full potential. A giant standing 6'5" and weighing 300 pounds, Dolegiewicz handled the following weights and repetitions in his workout.

Bishop Dolegiewicz regularly practiced squats in sets of ten repetitions with a 600-pound barbell, but the implement that tested his leg strength in a televised "world's strongest men" contest was more interesting. Dolegiewicz ranked among the world's best shot-putters and discus throwers, bench pressed 500 pounds for three repetitions, and power cleaned 400 pounds for two repetitions. *(Photo by Bruce Klemens)*

Bench Press	Squat	Power Clean
135 × 10	135 × 10	135 × 5
225 × 10	225 × 10	225 × 5
315 × 10	315 × 10	315 × 5
405 × 10	425 × 10	350 × 5
450 × 5–7	505 × 10	400 × 2
500 × 3	610 × 10 + 10 + 10	

Needless to say, only a bona fide superathlete could handle such poundages in a workout. Dolegiewicz's best single efforts in the three exercises were a 575-pound bench press, a 450-pound power clean, and around 700 pounds in the squat. When he reached that level in the squat he felt he had gone far enough; thereafter he concentrated on sets of ten for combined strength and cardiovascular training effect. In addition to the basic three, Dolegiewicz also practiced some curls and triceps extensions.

chapter four

exercises for specific muscles

Heretofore the emphasis has been on a three-exercise approach for developing overall functional strength and power, both for athletic conditioning and for general physical fitness. There are, of course, many other practical and useful weight training exercises.

FOR THE ABDOMINAL MUSCLES

One exercise practiced almost universally by athletes for abdominal muscle strength is the sit-up. These abdominal muscles should be kept toned throughout a lifetime to support the internal organs of the abdomen and prevent an imbalance of

49

torso muscle strength that often results in chronic low back pain.

The sit-up is an easy and a familiar exercise, but most people do not derive the best results from it because they don't do it properly. The exercise begins from a lying (supine) position with the legs bent and the feet anchored by a training partner or some heavy object. Assuming normal starting strength, you should clasp your hands at the back of your neck. (If it is too difficult for you to sit up with your hands behind the neck, begin by reaching forward with your arms as you sit up.) The main benefit of the sit-up comes at the very beginning of the exercise, when you should flatten your lower back against the surface you are resting on and attempt to move your head and shoulders toward your pelvis. As you do that, exhale, deliberately pull the abdomen in, and continue forward into a sitting position.

The abdominal muscles contract with the initial crunch and the contraction is intensified as you sit up. Continuing through the sit-up range also stretches the lower back muscles as it contracts the muscles of the abdomen. Abdominal muscles respond to exercise just as the other muscles of the body do, so it is not necessary to do great numbers of repetitions. Practical experience suggests that it does take a few more repetitions to

Sit-ups should be done with knees bent. The intensity of the exercise can be increased by using a slant board, as shown, and by holding a weight behind the neck.

exercise the abdomen than it does to exercise the arms, but twenty to thirty in a set seems to be plenty. When a set of twenty can be completed easily, the exercise is made more effective by holding a 5- or 10-pound weight behind the neck.

Competitors in the field events often exercise with heavy resistance in the sit-up, twisting first to the right and then to the left while sitting up. This adds strength to the turning movement involved in the throwing events.

STRENGTHENING THE LOWER LEGS

Athletes who do any running in their training (and most do) have little need of special exercises for the calf muscles. However, these muscles can be strengthened through a very simple exercise, an exercise that has been favored by some outstanding high jumpers (Dwight Stones, for example). The exercise is done by holding a barbell across the shoulders, as when squatting, standing with the toes and balls of the feet resting on a board (preferably at least two inches thick), and then alternately rising as high as possible on toes and sinking the heels as low as possible for complete contraction of the muscles and a full stretch.

The calf muscles are very dense and strong, so it is possible to use heavy weights in the rise-on-toes exercise. It is also advisable to do at least ten repetitions per set. Dwight Stones, a 6'5", 178-pound athlete who high-jumped 7 feet 7¼ inches and was a world record holder, used 250 pounds in the rise-on-toes exercise. Tom Woods, who was the same height and weight as Stones, and who high-jumped 7 feet 5½ inches, performed sets of ten in the exercise with 450, 500, 550, and 600 pounds. To place the poundages in perspective, Woods bench pressed 110 × 5, 130 × 5, 140 × 5, and 150 × 3. I believe 150 to 250 pounds is plenty of weight to use in exercising the calves and suspect other exercises Stones and Woods practiced contributed more to their jumping ability. Both practiced squats, for example, and Stones could clean and jerk 220 pounds.

To strengthen and stretch the calf muscles and tendons, stand with toes and the balls of the feet on a board, with the weight across your shoulders. Alternately rise as high as possible on your toes and sink to allow your heels to touch the floor. Nancy Borden demonstrates.

BICEPS CURLS

The biceps and allied muscles that flex the arms are of relatively little importance in most athletic events. They are important to pole vaulters and wrestlers, however, and it is advisable for other athletes to practice some arm flexing exercise if only to balance the extensor muscles, which are important in most sports. The biceps do thicken the upper arm, which improves leverage for shot-putters. It is also useful for runners to keep their biceps well toned because of the bent-arm position that is sustained while running.

The biceps can be exercised with a barbell or a pair of dumbbells. With a barbell you use an underhand grip (palms up, thumbs pointing outward) with hands placed approximately

52

shoulder width apart. Stand erect with the barbell across your upper thighs and your arms straight. Then simply flex your arms, bringing the weight in an arc from your thighs to your upper chest or throat—as far as it will go with your arms fully bent. Lower and do eight to ten repetitions for up to three sets. With dumbbells, hold the weights naturally at your sides (thumbs forward, palms in) and rotate the dumbbells as you flex your arms, turning your palms up as the weights rise. Lower and do eight to ten repetitions for up to three sets.

Pole vaulters should strive to handle as much weight as possible for the repetitions. Wrestlers should also try to increase the weight during the off-season. Fifty percent of body weight is plenty for curls, especially for more than five repetitions.

Vince Thompson demonstrates the start and finish of the barbell curl, an exercise for the arm flexors, primarily the biceps. Vince is a 6'1", 225-pound fullback who played four years of varsity football at Villanova University. As this book was being written, he was playing fullback for the Detroit Lions. Vince's weight training workout included five reps in the bench press with 315 pounds (best single: 375 pounds), five reps in the power clean with 205 pounds, and sets of ten in the squat with 315 pounds (best single: 525 pounds).

Jay Murray, one of the author's sons, demonstrates the rowing motion, a good exercise for developing pull-in strength for wrestling. Jay, who was a 177-pound letter-winning wrestler in college, holds a second-degree black belt in Isshinryu karate. Standing 6'1" and now weighing 210, Jay has power cleaned 320 pounds.

DEVELOPING THE UPPER BACK

Another exercise that develops the biceps and allied pulling muscles is the rowing motion, one of the best for strengthening the muscles of the upper back. The exercise can be done with a barbell or two dumbbells and is performed as follows: Hold the weight with an overhand grip (thumbs in), bend forward at the hips (back straight) with knees slightly bent to relieve strain, and let the weight hang directly down from your shoulders. Pulling with arm and upper back muscles, lift the weight to touch the upper part of the abdomen at the bottom of the rib cage. Three sets of eight to ten repetitions are recommended; 50–60 percent of body weight is a respectable poundage.

54

Try to confine the action to arm and upper back muscles, though this is difficult to do strictly with heavy weights. The rowing motion obviously is a good exercise for oarsmen and is also an excellent exercise for wrestlers, strengthening the pull-in effort used in takedowns and in riding an opponent. Many wrestlers strive to work up to body weight and more in rowing, though most athletes tend to involve considerable body motion with heavier weights.

Incidentally, pulling the weight up to the upper abdomen is the best general approach, but if you pull it up to the chest, the exercise affects the upper back muscles more. If you pull it to the waist, the exercise affects the middle and lower portion of the latissimus dorsi muscles more.

STRENGTHENING THE LOWER BACK

Both the power clean and the squat strengthen the lower back, but the best exercise to work that area directly with little likelihood of strain is a sort of reverse sit-up called the *back extension* or *hyperextension*. This exercise is done prone (face

Coach Nancy Borden demonstrates the back hyperextension exercise with Stacey Thompson, one of her runners, assisting. She starts with her forehead near the floor and arches upward as shown, holding a barbell plate behind her head.

down) with the legs anchored and the torso extended past the supporting surface (usually a bench; see photo). Start bending toward the floor and then arch up until your head and shoulders are slightly higher than your hips. Three sets of eight to ten repetitions each makes an effective program. Weight should be held behind the head whenever it becomes easy to complete ten. Twenty to 50 pounds is plenty, even for strong athletes, but it is possible to handle more with training. Weight lifters handle 100 pounds and more in the exercise.

SPECIAL EXERCISES FOR THE LEGS

Two useful leg exercises that cannot be performed with a barbell are the leg extension and the leg curl. Leg extensions have long been practiced to rehabilitate injured knees. The exercise strengthens the muscles that stabilize the knee without bringing the weight of the body to bear on the joint. Unless you have access to a leg extension/curl machine (often called a *knee machine* by athletic trainers), you will need a metal sandal, which is commercially available for about $15 to $20, to which a dumbbell bar or piece of pipe can be attached for loading barbell plates. The sandal, with weights attached, is strapped to the foot. Then you sit on a sturdy table high enough that the weight is suspended above the floor. Simply extend the leg until it is straight, tensing the thigh muscles, lower and repeat ten times for up to three sets.

To exercise the hamstrings—the biceps of the leg—stand on a step, bench, or sturdy box with the weighted foot hanging alongside. Flex the leg weighted by the sandal, curling the weight up backward toward the buttock. This exercise should also be done for ten repetitions for up to three sets.

The muscles at the front of the thigh, which extend the leg, are strong and permit more weight to be used for extensions than can be handled in leg curls. Most athletes will find they can use two to three times as much weight for the extension as for the curl. The amount of weight used isn't important, but it should be enough to make ten repetitions difficult to complete.

56

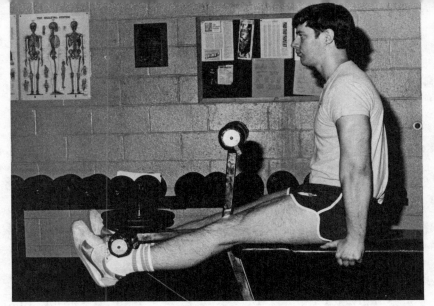

The leg extension exercise, shown on a "knee machine" apparatus, can also be performed using metal sandals, called *iron boots,* to which a dumbbell can be attached for additional resistance.

The thigh biceps (hamstrings) can also be exercised conveniently on a knee machine, or they can be worked at home with an iron boot (metal sandal) and extra weight. With the boot, the exercise is most effective when done standing or while lying with your head at the high end of a slant board.

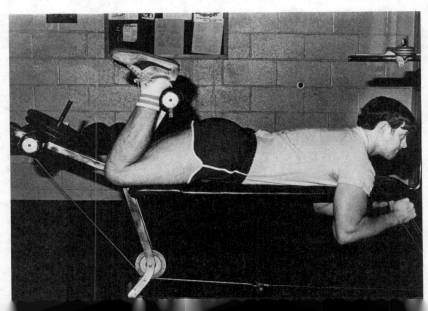

STRENGTHENING THE NECK

A strong neck is especially important for athletes in contact sports. Football players, wrestlers, rugby players, boxers—anyone likely to fall and tumble—should do at least one special neck exercise. One method involves using a purchased head harness (about $5–$8) from which a weight can be suspended while the neck is exercised by raising and lowering the head.

Another way to exercise the neck, possibly the best way, is the long-established wrestler's bridge exercise. The exercise is begun in a supine position with your feet drawn up close to the buttocks and your head on a pad (a mat or folded towel). Then you simply arch up, raising your torso from the floor and forcing your head against the padding until you are fully arched (bridged) and supported only by your feet and head. When it becomes easy to complete ten to fifteen repetitions, hold a 10-pound weight on your chest and increase the amount of weight whenever the exercise becomes easy. Be cautious to avoid injury with the wrestler's bridge, but don't underestimate the potential for the neck to develop muscular strength. George Hacken-schmidt, the old-time wrestling great, lifted a 311-pound barbell in the high bridge position, reaching back and pulling it up to his chest and then pressing it to the straight-arm position.

The wrestler's bridge, demonstrated by Vince Thompson, is one of the best exercises for strengthening the neck—especially important in sports like wrestling and football. Note that Vince is holding a barbell plate on his chest as he bridges.

STRENGTHENING THE WRISTS, HANDS, AND FINGERS

Wrist and grip strength are important in many sports. Whereas the effort of holding on to a barbell while practicing power cleans is very effective in strengthening the wrists and hands, some athletes may feel the need to do additional work to exercise them directly. The following two are among the best exercises for this purpose.

Wrist curls are done by raising and lowering a barbell, moving only the hands and fingers. Start in a kneeling position, with forearms supported across a bench, hands and wrists extending past the support. Hold a light barbell with an underhand grip (thumbs outward). Allow the hands and fingers to hang down, fingers almost open but curved just enough to avoid dropping the barbell. Then raise the barbell as high as possible without forearm movement. Start by closing the fingers to grip the barbell firmly and continue to raise the weight by bending the hands as far upward as they will go. Experiment with light weights (15 to 25 pounds) until you find out how much is needed to tax the strength of your fingers and hands with ten repetitions.

The same exercise can be done with an overhand grip, except, of course, that the fingers can't be opened.

A better way to exercise the other side of the forearm (the forearm muscles strengthen the wrist and grip) is to perform *reverse curls,* as follows: Stand and hold a barbell across your thighs with an overhand grip (thumbs in), arms hanging straight. Cock your hands toward your thighs by bending your hands inward at the wrists, then deliberately cock them away from you and follow through by bringing the barbell in an arc to your upper chest, using only arm strength (no swinging).

The reverse curl begins as a palms-down wrist curl and continues as a complete exercise for the arm flexors, except that the biceps are in an inefficient position. This puts more stress on

Vince Thompson shows how to perform wrist curls, to strengthen the hands, wrists, and forearms. In the palms-up position, as shown, the fingers can be allowed to open almost all the way. When the exercise is done with palms down, of course, the fingers must remain closed and only the hands move up and down.

Another good grip strengthener is the reverse curl,
done like the regular curl but with palms down.

the forearms, especially at the point near the elbow. Experiment
to find a weight that is challenging for ten repetitions.

The wrist curl and reverse curl exercises can be added to the
workout of any athlete who feels his or her grip is deficient.
Wrist and forearm exercises have traditionally been popular with
baseball players, who believe these movements help with the
final whip of the bat and make it possible to hit with more
power.

DUMBBELL EXERCISES

As mentioned earlier, some of the exercises described here and performed with barbells also can be done with dumbbells, short-handled implements that allow the hands to move separately. An adjustable dumbbell set that can be loaded from 2½ to 42½ pounds in increments of 2½ pounds can be purchased by mail

To strengthen the muscles at the sides of the shoulders, dumbbells should be raised laterally as shown in the photos. Note the slight forward lean and downward tilt of the front ends of the dumbbells to focus the exercise on the sides rather than the fronts of the deltoid muscles. The front deltoids receive plenty of exercise in the bench press and overhead presses.

order for about $45 to $50, plus freight. Additional plates can be loaded on the handles, so it is possible to load such a set to 100 pounds or more on each dumbbell by using 25-pound plates.

For the dumbbell exercises described on the following pages, however, less than 40 pounds each will be ample for even strong men. The first is an exercise for the side portion of the shoulder muscle. The entire shoulder (deltoid) muscle is activated by exercising with various forms of pressing weights overhead, but if additional strength is needed, an exercise called the lateral raise, standing, is highly effective. The exercise begins with two dumbbells held at the sides of the legs, with knuckles out (thumbs forward). From this point, raise the weights directly out at your sides, keeping knuckles up and tipping the front ends of the dumbbells slightly downward as the weights reach shoulder height. The elbows may be bent slightly. It also helps to focus on the sides of the shoulders if you lean forward a bit. It is not necessary to raise the dumbbells any higher than an inch or two above shoulder level, since the deltoids are fully activated by the time the elbows reach shoulder height with the arms out at the sides.

Ten repetitions of the lateral raise, standing, should be done for one to three sets, depending on the athlete's needs. This exercise is especially valuable for discus throwers, who throw with arms extended to the side, and for swimmers, who must repeatedly lift their arms out of the water to reach for the next stroke.

A second useful exercise that can be performed only with dumbbells is another lateral raise—the lateral raise, lying, also referred to as the *flying exercise,* because the motion is like the inverted action of a bird's wings. This exercise is done lying on a bench, beginning with the dumbbells held straight up over the chest. From that point, you bend your elbows slightly and, with control, lower the weights as far as possible to the side and then bring them back to the starting point. This exercise, like the lateral raise, standing, builds strength for throwing the discus.

More weight can be used in the lying position than while standing, because both the front deltoid and the big pectoral

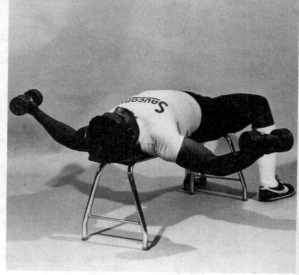

The bent-arm lateral raise, lying ("flying exercise"), should be done as shown, with arms slightly bent throughout. This is an exercise that is useful to discus throwers and swimmers.

muscles of the chest are involved when you are in the supine position. Good results can be obtained with from 10 to 20 pounds on each dumbbell, but strong athletes have handled up to 40 pounds or more. In the standing position, 10 to 30 pounds will produce good results, but some men do work up to even heavier weights. The flying exercise is also done for ten repetitions for up to three sets.

A VARIATION ON THE BENCH PRESS

In addition to the basic bench press exercise done on a flat bench, throwers can benefit from practicing presses on an incline that approximates the 30 to 45 degrees at which implements are delivered—the shot and discus, in particular. The exercise also adds development to the upper part of the pectoral muscle, which provides protective padding for football players whose chest muscles do not develop adequate thickness from the regular bench press.

Pressing on an incline, as shown, is a good exercise for shot-putters, discus throwers, and javelin throwers, as well as for football players (to build protective muscle across the upper chest). The exercise can be done with a barbell, as shown, or with a pair of dumbbells.

Performance is simple. Take the barbell from supports at the elevated head end of the bench, or have it lifted high by training partners so as to start with the barbell straight up at arms' length. (Pressing the barbell straight up while on an incline provides the proper angle for the muscular action.) Lower the barbell to touch the upper chest near the clavicles and immediately push the barbell back up to the straight-arm position. The exercise also can be done with a pair of dumbbells, and there may be an advantage in using the independent hand weights because they allow a greater and more natural range of motion. Many successful shot-putters and discus throwers have included heavy barbell incline presses in their workouts, however; so the exercise obviously produces good results with a bar or dumbbells.

The weight should be heavy enough, after a light warm-up set of eight to ten, to limit the repetitions to five to eight for three sets.

EXTENSION EXERCISES FOR THE TRICEPS

The triceps muscles of the back of the arms are strengthened by any exercise that straightens the arms, so they respond to bench presses, especially with hands placed close together on the bar, and presses. If they need additional work—and many shot-putters and javelin throwers believe they do—extension exercises focus directly on them. One way to do extensions is to hold a weight directly overhead, with hands close together. Lower the weight behind your neck and then force it back overhead again, keeping your elbows stationary and pointed directly upward throughout. This form of extension is a particularly good one because it provides good stretch for the triceps as well as strong contraction. You can either use a barbell, with hands no farther apart than six inches, or a dumbbell, with both hands around one end, as shown in the photos.

Another way to do extensions is in the supine position. Start

Triceps extensions, as demonstrated by Nancy Borden, are valuable for shot-putters and javelin throwers. The exercise can be done with a dumbbell, as shown, or with a barbell, using a close grip. The elbows actually should be pointing a little more nearly straight up when the weight is lowered than is shown.

with your arms pointing straight above your chest and lower the weight to touch your forehead lightly. Then force it back to the straight-arm position, again keeping the elbows stationary and pointing up throughout. Obviously, a dumbbell is inappropriate for the supine version.

Extensions should be done for eight to ten repetitions with a weight that is appropriate for the repetitions.

67

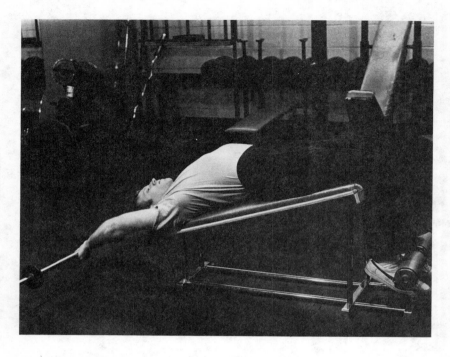

The pullover exercise, done on a decline, is a good one for swimmers, gymnasts, and pole vaulters. Swimmers should use relatively light weights (20 to 40 pounds) and vaulters and gymnasts should try to handle heavier poundages (50 to 80 pounds and more).

A SPECIAL EXERCISE FOR SWIMMERS

Just as distance runners must spend most of their training time running, swimmers must spend most of theirs in the water. Strength is an asset in swimming, too, however, and the basic strength builders develop it in minimal time. As mentioned previously, the lateral raise is a good exercise for swimmers; so is a simple variation on a standard bodybuilding exercise—the pullover, but done head down on a slant board.

Lying on a board at about a 30- to 45-degree angle, with feet anchored at the top by a strap, hold a light barbell with arms straight and directly above your chest. (Your arms will be pointed somewhat toward your feet, because of the board's angle.) Now lower the weight with straight or slightly bent arms to touch the floor or the base of the board below your head. Immediately pull the weight back to the starting position. Place your hands less than shoulder width apart (twelve inches or fewer) and inhale while lowering the weight; exhale as it is pulled back to the starting position. The weight need not be heavy. Twenty pounds will be plenty for most people, but you should experiment to determine how much is needed to feel the work in three sets of ten repetitions.

Just as the lateral raise strengthens the muscles that lift the arms to reach forward for the next stroke, the pullover, in a declined position, strengthens the muscles that pull the stroke down through the water. It is not necessary to simulate the stroke closely; the important thing is to strengthen the appropriate muscles and practice swimming.

THE HAMMER THROW EXERCISES

Key exercises for hammer throwers are power cleans and squats. Bench presses are less useful for this particular event than pressing weights overhead. But another exercise is especially useful for this event that is little practiced (or needed) by athletes in other events who practice the power clean. The

Shrugs, as demonstrated by Bert Marchio, involve minimal movement—just a raising and lowering of the shoulders—but the exercise is a good one for hammer throwers to practice.

exercise is the shoulder shrug, a simple movement in which a relatively heavy barbell is held across the upper thighs, with arms hanging straight down, and then raised as high as possible by shrugging the shoulders upward. The weight should be as heavy as possible while still allowing perceptible movement. (There's no point in holding such a heavy weight that all you can do is *try* to shrug!) Three sets of ten repetitions each should be done for this exercise, which focuses on the trapezius muscles running from the neck to the shoulders.

Shrugs, incidentally, are also useful for developing protective muscle for football players and wrestlers, in conjunction with bridging or headstrap exercises. However, they are seldom needed by athletes who do power cleans unless they are particularly susceptible to neck or shoulder injuries.

PRESSING WEIGHTS OVERHEAD

In recent years the bench press has become a favorite exercise of weight trainers because it is the most effective single upper body exercise, because ego-satisfying weights can be used, and probably because it is done lying down. But before bench pressing became popular, the most effective single shoulder and arm exercise was the standing press, in which a barbell or pair of dumbbells is cleaned to the shoulders (as in the power clean) and then, with no assistance from the legs, pushed overhead to the straight-arm position. This is still an excellent exercise but need not be strongly emphasized by an athlete who is doing a lot of bench pressing. For someone who does not have an exercise bench, however, the standing press can be substituted as

The barbell press, demonstrated by Bill Grochowicz, Director of Operations at the Plainfield Area (New Jersey) YMCA, is one of the best exercises for developing the shoulders and arms.

a key exercise in the basic three. In this case the logical progression is to do the presses first, then the power cleans—with heavier weights—and finally the squats. For example:

Press   50% of limit × 8–10
             60% × 5
             70% × 5
             80% × 3
             85% × 3
             90% × 1–3

Power   50% of limit × 5
Clean   60% × 5
             70% × 5
             80% × 3
             90% × 1–3

Squat   50% of limit × 10
             60% × 8
             70% × 8
             80% × 5
             90% × 5

If you have no other equipment but a barbell, you can follow the above workout, but the weight you use in the squats will be limited to the poundage you can place on your shoulders unassisted *and remove unassisted after completing the squats.* (While serving in the South Pacific during World War II, I frequently worked out alone with only a crude barbell made by the SeaBees. I can recall that it was quite difficult to clean and jerk 210 pounds—10 pounds more than I weighed at the time at age nineteen—lower it behind my neck, squat ten repetitions, and then still have enough energy in the tropical heat to jerk it from behind my neck and set it down. It is much better to obtain squat stands, or have two training partners lift the weight

The start of the dumbbell press is demonstrated by Rich Hart, pictured at age 14, weighing 175 pounds at 5'9". The press with dumbbells is a favorite exercise of Rich's, who demonstrated great athletic potential as a junior high school football player (guard/linebacker) and baseball player.

Completion of the press with dumbbells is shown by Dick Hart, father of Rich Hart. Note that the dumbbells rotate from fore-and-aft to side-to-side as they go up. Dick Hart, who put the shot more than 64 feet in high school, establishing a record that stood for twenty years, was signed to a major league baseball bonus contract, and later earned a starting position (at guard) with the Philadelphia Eagles.

shoulder high, or simply use less weight so you have an ample reserve to get it off your shoulders at the end of the exercise.)

If you are doing a full workout with all the essential equipment, and you are basing your routine on the clean/bench press/squat triad, it is still worthwhile to practice some overhead pressing to improve overall shoulder strength. If you are doing a complete routine of heavy bench presses, doing three sets of six to eight repetitions in the standing press will provide added benefits without overworking your shoulder and arm muscles.

chapter five

basic programs for specific sports

As you have seen, although weight programs for athletes can be based on three key exercises, a number of other exercises can be added for specific needs of athletic specialists. In addition, certain exercises can also be added by individual athletes to overcome specific shortcomings. The following are programs of general usefulness to athletes in various sports. No effort has been made to account for individual deficiencies, however, and an athlete whose grip is not as strong as he might like it to be should add wrist curls or wrist curls and the reverse barbell curl—two to three sets of ten in each exercise. An athlete with weak calf muscles should add three sets, ten repetitions each, of the rise-on-toes. As another example, a swimmer might want to strengthen his chest muscles additionally by including two or three sets of the flying exercise (the bent-arm lateral raise, lying on a bench). An endless variety of training programs can be designed to meet individual needs, but the following approaches will serve very well for athletes with no special problems.

A program for football players and weight men (shot put, discus, javelin, and hammer throw):

When percentages are given in parentheses (%) they refer to the athlete's best single effort in the lift. A person who could power clean 200 pounds once, as a limit effort, would begin this program by cleaning 120 pounds five times, then progress to 140 pounds for five, and so on. Remember, this is a general approach; with the onset of staleness you should switch to a cycled approach for the three key exercises (see page 40).

Power Clean
5 (60%) + 5 (70%) + 5 (75%) + 3 (80%) + 2–3 (85%) + 1–2 (90%)
Bench Press
10 (50%) + 5 (70%) + 5 (80%) + 3 (90%) + 1–2 (95%)
Squat
10 (50%) + 10 (70%) + 5 (80%) + 3 sets of 5 (85%)
Sit-Up
20–30 repetitions (add weight, held behind head, when 30 becomes easy)
Curl
2–3 sets of 8–10 repetitions with weight appropriate to reps
Triceps Extension
2–3 sets of 8–10 reps, with appropriate weight
Lateral Raise
2–3 sets of 10 with appropriate weight
Overhead Press
2–3 sets of 6–8 with appropriate weight

The strength program should be followed three days per week in the off-season—Monday, Wednesday, and Friday or Tuesday,

Thursday, and Saturday—with some jogging and faster running on two or three alternate days.

A program for team sports involving running, jumping, and throwing (basketball, volleyball, lacrosse, soccer, and baseball; also appropriate for hockey):

The running, throwing, and skating sports emphasize skill, speed, and endurance, so ample time must be spent practicing the skills until the movements become quick and sure. But strength will prove an asset in any and all of these sports. The strength program should be followed two to three days per week, and running and skills should be practiced on at least three alternate days if not every day. (Once the actual season begins, of course, skills will be practiced daily under a coach's direction and strength work should be reduced to a maintenance level—50 percent to 70 percent at most—two days per week or discontinued entirely if team practice becomes too demanding.)

Power Clean
    5 (50%) + 5 (60%) + 3 (75%) + 3 (80%) + 2 sets of 3 (85%)
Bench Press
    10 (50%) + 10 (65%) + 5–8 (75%)
Squat
    10 (50%) + 5 (70%) + 5 (75%) + 5 (80%)
Sit-Up
    20 repetitions (hold weight behind head when 20 becomes easy)
Curl
    10 + 10 with weight appropriate to the repetitions
Lateral Raise
    10 + 10 with appropriate weights (5- to 15-pound dumbbells)
Press
    2 sets of 6–8 with appropriate weight

A program for wrestlers:

Wrestling requires a combination of strength and endurance—and, of course, great skill. Wrestlers should follow a strength program three days a week with extensive running on alternate days. Once actual practice is seriously under way, the amounts lifted should be cut by about 10 percent.

Power Clean
　　10 (60%) + 8 (70%) + 3 sets of 5 (75%)
Bench Press
　　10 (60%) + 10 (70%) + 3 sets of 8 (75%)
Squat
　　10 (50%) + 10 (65%) + 3 sets of 10 (75%)
Sit-Up
　　2 sets of 20–30 (add weight, held behind head,
　　when 30 becomes easy)
Curl
　　3 sets of 10 with appropriate weight for the repetitions
Lateral Raise
　　3 sets of 10 with appropriate weight
Rowing
　　3 sets of 10 with appropriate weight
Press
　　3 sets of 6–8 with appropriate weight
Wrestler's Bridge
　　3 sets of 10 (hold weight on chest after first set)

A program for sprinters, hurdlers, and jumpers:

Sprinters, hurdlers, and jumpers (long, high, and triple) need explosive power, so they should train much as the track and field weight men do. A few years ago, when he held the world record in his event, high-jumper Dwight Stones trained on heavy cleans and squats. The tall, rangy Stones had poor leverage for weight lifting but cleaned some 40 pounds more than his own weight and practiced squats with comparable poundages.

Russ Hodge, former world record holder in the decathlon, told a reporter for *Power & Fitness* magazine that he had improved his 100-yard dash time from 9.8 to 9.3 through heavy leg work. "My fastest 100 meters, incidentally, was run during the winter, a week after I did a best-ever squat," Hodge said. A 220-pounder who ran 100 meters in 10.2, Hodge did a partial squat, "almost parallel," with 775 pounds.

Power Clean
   5 (50%) + 5 (65%) + 3 (80%) + 2 (85%) + 1–2 (90%)
Bench Press
   10 (50%) + 5 (70%) + 3–5 (80%) + 1–3 (90%)
Squat
   10 (50%) + 8 (65%) + 5 (75%) + 5 (80%)
Sit-Up
   20–30 repetitions (add weight, held behind head, when 30 is easy)
Curl
   10 + 10 with weight appropriate to the repetitions
Press
   8–10 + 5–8 with appropriate weights

A program for swimmers:

Swimmers will benefit from the same exercises as other athletes, with the addition of one special exercise—provided they spend ample time in the water perfecting their strokes and kicks and obtaining the specific conditioning that is necessary in all sports. Because they need to expend prodigious amounts of energy in the water, swimmers should keep their strength programs as brief and basic as possible.

Power Clean
   5 (50%) + 5 (60%) + 5 (70%)
Bench Press
   10 (50%) + 10 (60%) + 10 (70%)

Squat
> 10 (50%) + 10 (65%) + 10 (75%)

Pullover, decline position
> 10 pullovers after each set of squats, with appropriate weight

Sit-Up
> 20–30 repetitions (add weight, held behind head, when 30 is easy)

Lateral Raise
> 3 sets of 10 with appropriate weight

Flying Exercise (optional)
> 2–3 sets of 10 with appropriate weight

Press
> 8–10 with appropriate weight

A program for the racquet sports:

The racquet sports—tennis, squash, and racquetball—call primarily for skill, quickness, and conditioning achieved primarily by practicing the games themselves. Strength is an asset in any sport, however, so people interested in these activities would benefit from brief weight training workouts. A recommended approach follows.

Power Clean
> 10 (50%) + 5 (65%)

Bench Press
> 10 (60%)

Squat
> 10 (60%)

Sit-Up
> 20 repetitions (twisting alternately, touching elbow to opposite knee)

Curl
> 10 repetitions with weight appropriate for the repetitions

Press

    10 repetitions with weight appropriate for the repetitions

Wrist Curl

    10 + 10 + 10 with palms up

    10 + 10 + 10 with palms down

A program for gymnasts:

Gymnasts must be very strong, and sometimes it is difficult to begin the demanding practice sessions without first building a foundation of strength. The following program should be practiced with progressively heavier weights as the basic gymnastic skills are learned, until the athlete develops enough strength to derive full benefit from the extremely strenuous practice of the skills.

Power Clean

    10 (50%) + 8 (60%) + 6 (70%)

Bench Press

    10 (50%) + 8 (60%) + 6 (70%)

One-Quarter Squat (halfway to parallel)

    10 + 10 + 10 (beginning with 50% of body weight and
    working up to body weight plus 25% as you become
    conditioned)

Sit-Up

    30 (hold weight behind head when 30 becomes easy)

Lateral Raise

    10 + 10 + 10 with appropriate weight for the repetitions

Decline Pullover

    10 + 10 + 10 with as much weight as possible for the
    repetitions

Press

    10 + 8 + 6 with increasing weights

Rowing

    10 + 10 + 10 with appropriate weight

A program for pole vaulters:

A pole vaulter must be a combination sprinter and gymnast, approaching the vault with speed and then achieving body control with a pull-push motion during the vault itself. As a result, vaulters must achieve great upper body strength as well as powerful legs. Repeated fast runs of 50, 100, 200, and 300 meters should be part of training for pole vaulters. The following weight training approach will provide the additional strength needed.

Power Clean
    5 (50%) + 5 (65%) + 3 (80%) + 1–2 (85%–90%)
Bench Press
    10 (50%) + 5 (70%) + 3–5 (80%)
One-Quarter Squat (halfway to parallel)
    10 (50%) + 8 (65%) + 5 (75%) + 5 (80%)
Rowing
    8–10 repetitions with appropriate weight, 3 sets
Sit-Up
    20–30 (twisting, weight behind head)
Curl
    8–10 reps with appropriate weight, 3 sets
Press
    10 + 8 + 6 + 4 (increase weight for each set)
Chin
    3 sets of as many as possible

chapter six

a program for all—athletes and nonathletes

By now the reader must be aware that there is little difference among the programs suggested for different sports. This is intentional. All kinds of specialized approaches have been devised, but the programs in this book closely resemble those that good athletes actually use. Enough examples have been cited to make it clear that the simple, basic approach works for outstanding performers in a variety of sports.

In reading this book and applying the information provided, try to evaluate yourself objectively. Are you a large, heavy-boned person like shot-putters George Woods and Bishop

Dolegiewicz, a more intermediate type such as jumper/sprinter Tommy Haynes, or a rangy type like high-jumpers Dwight Stones and Tom Woods? If you are around 6' tall and measure 8 inches around the wrist, you are destined to be husky and only the most favorable genetic neuromuscular endowment is going to give you great speed and endurance while moving a massive framework. If you are 5'9" tall with a 7-inch wrist, your chance of becoming an interior lineman in professional football is slim, regardless of how strong and quick you are. And if you are 6'4" or taller with a wrist that measures 7½ inches at most, you ought to be thinking about basketball or the high jump. Look back through the book at the types of programs followed by people who most closely resemble you. The chances are that those are the programs you will thrive on as well.

In addition to the approach used by athletes who are about your size, you will have to find out by trial and error how you respond to various intensities of exercise and how these bouts of exercise are best mixed with rest to produce the optimum results for you. This is one of the hardest things to do and can be done best if you have an intelligent, observant coach and/or training partner. Unfortunately, most coaches insist that everyone train alike. This generally results in a lot of athletes going stale and a few gluttons for punishment not getting enough work.

The percentage system described earlier is a good general approach, but individuals will have to modify it according to their own responses. Interviewed by *Power & Fitness* magazine, Russ Hodge, the former decathlon great, mentioned that weight lifting champion Russ Knipp had helped him with a percentage program in which he worked from 50 to 80 percent levels and tried limit singles only every six weeks or so. But Hodge found by experience that he needed to work at somewhat higher percentages than Knipp to keep his strength up. He attributed the need for higher percentages to the fact that he was running a lot, which tended to reduce his strength. There are many others, however, who would find they would have to reduce the total amount of weight training they were doing if they were also doing a lot of running. Each individual is different and each must find the ideal mix of weight training, other exercise such as running or skill practice, and rest.

Incidentally, I accidentally learned that I was habitually overtraining and needed to cycle down much more. During my junior year of college I had late classes every day but Tuesday, which was the only day except meet day—Saturday—that I could get out to the track and practice with the javelin. I exercised with dumbbells in my room and, with only one day of throwing practice per week, had my best collegiate season. Later I threw the javelin farther in AAU competition with even less practice, training primarily for weight lifting. For me, as an individual, minimal hard throwing practice and a lot of strength training produced the best results. You might think that would have taught me something, but I made the mistake of training too intensively on lifting as well, trying myself out on Wednesdays for Saturday contests. As a result, I never did as well on Saturday as on Wednesday and my overall progress suffered until I greatly moderated the intensity of my training. This experience, plus observation of training trends, is the basis for my recommending cycling workouts.

On the other hand, one young man I trained primarily for football was an absolute glutton for hard workouts. Dave Neeld also thrived on them. He would go through his basic program (to a best single power clean of 290, bench press of 355, and repetition squats with 350) and do so many sets of ten repetitions in presses and curls that I would get tired watching him. It worked for Dave. He won a couple of Middle Atlantic AAU weight lifting championships on raw power, was named NAIA all-district linebacker two years in a row at Appalachian State, then switched to fullback and averaged 130 yards per game as a senior. By the way, Dave was not really big enough to play linebacker, at 5'9½" and 190–195 pounds, but the people he tackled were glad he wasn't any bigger. In addition to being very strong, he had a best time for 40 yards of 4.5 seconds.

THE NONATHLETE OR EX-ATHLETE

The exercise approach described in this book can also be adapted to a keep-fit routine for ex-athletes and nonathletes. For this kind of program, you can moderate the weights and add jogging or fast walking for an efficient cardiovascular/respiratory counterpoint to the muscle toning. The percentages below are based on lifts made by athletes while in serious training during an athletic prime.

Monday-Wednesday-Friday
  Power Clean: 5 (50%) + 5 (55%) + 5 (60%) + 3 (65%)
  Bench Press: 10 (40%) + 8 (45%) + 6 (50%) + 4 (55%) + 2 (60%–70%)
  Squat: 10 (40%) + 8 (45%) + 6 (50%) + 4 (55%) + 2 (60%–70%)
  Rowing: 2–3 sets of 8–10 repetitions
  Curl: 2–3 sets of 8–10 repetitions
  Press: 2–3 sets of 6–8 repetitions

Same days or Tuesday-Thursday-Saturday
  Jog or jog/run or walk/run 20–30 minutes
           OR
  Walk briskly 30 minutes or longer

A keep-fit routine varies according to the ambition and age of the exerciser. When I was in my thirties I could jog comfortably at less than two minutes per quarter mile, do three repetition power cleans with 250 pounds, and do other lifts in proportion. In my early forties I slowed the jog by about fifteen seconds per quarter and found I could power clean 250 pounds only once. In my fifties old football injuries caused my knees to protest jogging at any speed, so I switched to walking a two-mile course in a half hour. And I stopped going past 200 pounds for repetition power cleans (though I did jerk 250 overhead to

Pictured practicing power cleans at age 38, Dick Hart used the same kinds of exercises to keep fit after retiring from professional football that he used for preseason conditioning.

commemorate turning 55, taking the weight from squat stands). Tapering off is an individual thing and will depend on your own body's reaction.

To give the reader an idea how a super athlete tapers off, Dick Hart—former pro football player—was working out with his son, Rich, a 14-year-old junior high school football and baseball player as this book was being written. At 38, Dick could do repetition power cleans with weights ranging from 250 to 280 pounds and singles to 300 pounds. He squatted for repetitions to 400 pounds and did standing presses to 240 to 260

A father and son training program is an excellent way for ex-athletes to keep in shape and for youngsters to build for the future. Here Rich Hart, age 14, squats with 200 pounds (though he has done 300) while his father stands by as a spotter.

pounds, depending on how ambitious he felt at the time. This sounds like a murderous workout for a 38-year-old—or at any age, for that matter!—but for a man who cleaned 335 pounds a few years earlier, it was tapering off.

A person who has never been a serious athlete can follow the program on a basis of experimentally determined maximum lifts. A word of caution: If you have not been actively athletic over the years and are no longer in your teens or twenties, proceed with deliberate care. Great benefit can be derived from weight training mixed with jogging or fast walking, but the approach must be gradual. It makes no sense to proceed to an all-out single effort in the power clean, bench press, or squat if you are 30 or 40 or older and have allowed yourself to get completely out of condition. Instead, proceed very conservatively to work out with weights you can lift at least twice with reasonable comfort—a good effort, but short of straining. Base your percentages on a "vigorous double" rather than on an all-out single lift.

If you have any doubt whatsoever about your fitness to begin an exercise program, get a physician's okay before proceeding. And try to find a physician who is sympathetic to and knowledgeable about exercise. Most doctors know at least a little about jogging but zilch about weight training. Chances are that if a doctor says you're fit to jog and you have no special orthopedic problems, you're also fit to train with weights.

GENERAL CONDITIONING AND HEALTH RECOMMENDATIONS

Several times I've mentioned that in addition to a properly balanced training program—hard enough to get results but not so hard as to produce staleness—you need to follow other sensible good-health guidelines. One of these is to get enough rest. An athlete in training needs about eight hours of sleep a night, though there are many people who seem to thrive on about seven. But rest is more than just getting enough sleep. It is also important to have an occasional day—preferably at least one day a week—in which you do nothing that is really strenuous.

Some people need more recovery time than others, so if you find you become increasingly tired using a six-day training program—alternating weight training and running with one day off from both—cut back to a five-day program. If developing strength is your primary goal, cut your running days to two. If speed and/or endurance is more important to you, run three days and train with weights on two. Or alternate weeks: three days of weight training and two days of running one week; two days of weight training and three days of running the next.

With a six-day program, you might train with weights on Monday, Wednesday, and Friday and run on Tuesday, Thursday, and Saturday. A five-day program emphasizing strength would include weight training Monday, Wednesday, and Saturday and running Tuesday and Thursday. A five-day program emphasizing speed and endurance would include running Monday, Wednesday, and Friday and weight training Tuesday and Saturday.

It is also possible to practice running (or skill practice that involves running) five days a week and weight training two or three days. Serious distance runners train with roadwork or on the track almost every day and work with weights three days a week, but that is a very specialized approach that would wear down most people and would not be conducive to success in any other sport.

One simple way to determine if you are training too hard and not getting enough rest is to take your pulse first thing in the morning every day. Just sit on the edge of the bed upon awakening, count your pulse for fifteen seconds, and multiply by four. Or count for thirty seconds and multiply by two. If your pulse gets faster two days in a row, you either need to reduce the intensity of your training or take a day off.

An "average normal" pulse is seventy-two heartbeats per

minute. As physical condition improves, the pulse gets *slower* and the heart beats more strongly and efficiently. If you are checking your pulse and find that, with training, the rate gradually drops from seventy-two to seventy to sixty-eight and lower, that indicates your condition is improving. Obviously, it can't keep dropping indefinitely—it's very important that your heart continue to beat! But a pulse in the low sixties indicates superior fitness; some distance runners in top shape for their event have resting pulses of fifty beats per minute and less.

If you are checking your pulse regularly and note a drop from, say, seventy-two to sixty-six over a period of time and then a leveling off, that's fine. But if your pulse rate starts back up again and is sixty-eight to seventy for a couple of days in a row, it's an indication that you're either training too hard or not getting enough rest between workouts.

A field events athlete or football player on a between-seasons strength program, striving to build size and power, with an "average" resting pulse of seventy-two, should consider adding some endurance training for general conditioning, even if it's only an easy twenty-minute jog two or three days a week.

INTEGRATING RUNNING WITH STRENGTH TRAINING

To begin a general conditioning program on non–weight training days, start by doing some easy jogging *every day* for a week at a pace that will allow you to continue for fifteen to twenty minutes in reasonable comfort. The reason for the everyday approach at first is to prevent stiffness and soreness from building up in your calf muscles, ankles, and feet. During that first week, any time your breathing becomes labored, ease off to a walk until you feel able to jog comfortably again. Jog on a soft surface, wearing running shoes that fit well and have well-padded soles. During that first week, reduce the poundages on your three weight training days to 70–80 percent of what you were using before you began to jog.

The second week and thereafter, cut the jogging back to three days per week, alternating with weight training days, leaving one day free of both weight training and jogging.

This approach can be varied to include a mixture of jogging and running, and there is some advantage in faster running for its contribution to speed and power. A mixed jogging/running program on a track might include the following.

1. Half-mile (two-lap) jog to warm up.
2. Walk the turns, picking up to a jog as you approach the straightaways, and then accelerate into a full run for about 40–50 yards, finishing by easing off to a jog and then a walk around the turn before repeating the jog/run/jog. Repeat the walk/jog/run sequence for a total of two or three laps.
3. Alternately run a half lap (220 yards) at about 60–75 percent speed and walk a half lap for a total of two or three laps.
4. Jog a half mile to cool down.

The approach outlined above is for athletes who are primarily seeking strength and power, to provide general cardiovascular/respiratory conditioning, and for people who want to mix weight training and running for general fitness. I would not presume to instruct serious runners about running. There are many fine references available that cover training for running in detail, a subject that is outside the scope of this book (see Appendix).

It is also worth emphasizing that this book is for the athlete and fitness seeker who does not have access to coaching or experienced, knowledgeable training partners. The advice on weight training is sound, generally applicable, and should be helpful to coaches as well as athletes. But how the weight training is integrated into specific programs for specific events or sports will vary according to the coach's approach and the athlete's individual needs.

chapter seven
nutrition and drugs

I've covered nutrition and drugs in some detail in two of my earlier books, *Inside Weight Lifting and Weight Training* and *Inside Bodybuilding* (both published by Contemporary Books, Inc.), but I'll summarize important points here. First, strive for a balanced diet of natural foods. Second, avoid drugs unless a doctor prescribes them for a specific illness.

A balanced diet would include some from each of seven groups of foods:

1. Leafy green vegetables and yellow vegetables, which provide vitamins (especially vitamin B) and minerals.
2. Citrus fruits, tomatoes, raw cabbage, and salad greens, which provide vitamin C and roughage.

3. Potatoes and similar root vegetables, as well as fruits, to provide starch, vitamins, and minerals.
4. Milk and such milk products as cheese are sources of calcium and protein.
5. Meat, poultry, fish, eggs, and legumes for protein and minerals.
6. Bread, flour, and cereals to provide energy, vitamins, iron, and minerals.
7. Butter, margarine, and vegetable oil to provide vitamin A and oil.

Many diet fads have gained popularity among athletes (and nonathletes, for that matter) and they will probably continue to do so. Most of them seem pointless in view of the wide variety of diets consumed by champion athletes from different parts of the world.

It is also important to obtain ample fluid replacement when you are training hard and perspiring. Any coach who says you shouldn't drink water when you're thirsty is a relic from the Dark Ages.

There may be some value in special supplements, to compensate for the intense physical activity of athletes in hard training. A multivitamin tablet may prevent an unsuspected deficiency, for example, and certainly does no harm. The jury is still out on the value of large doses of vitamins—vitamin C, for example—but there are intelligent and knowledgeable people who believe most people receive less than optimal amounts of vitamin C and other nutrients. Vitamin E, as an aid to boosting endurance, is another supplement that has its advocates. One way to assure proper nutrition is to try to include some foods from each of the seven major groups daily.

DRUGS

Make no mistake about it, we do live in a "drug culture."

People seek their kicks with drugs, and increasingly athletes seem to be using drugs because they believe they will provide them with an advantage over their competitors. I am unable to discuss this kind of drug use objectively, because I consider it so disgusting as to be beneath recognition. But it is there, so I'll discuss it—though not objectively.

I was present in the 1950s when one of the "pioneers" in the use of anabolic steroids experimented on athletes who volunteered for the tests. There was *no detectable improvement* in any of the test subjects, who included a Mr. America winner and a national weight lifting champion, both of whom had won their titles before the experiments.

Aside from my forty-year background in athletic training, I also have more than twenty years of experience as a medical writer and am acutely aware of the extreme difficulty legitimate scientists have in proving that therapeutic compounds produce benefits that outweigh their risks. If *anything* worked as well as the proponents of anabolic steroids say they work—without significant adverse effects—we would have a nation of superpeople. All athletes would be record breakers, average people would be strong, and the aged would not be infirm. Instead, these drugs that supposedly produce supermen and superwomen are considered only "probably" effective as adjunctive therapy for senile and postmenopausal osteoporosis, degenerative illnesses they were painstakingly developed to treat.

And the anabolic steroids do present hazards. They can be toxic to the liver, for example, and they can inhibit the natural production of male hormones in normally healthy men. The long-term hazards of these potent compounds won't be known for another twenty to thirty years, when the current crop of 20- to 30-year-old seekers for the shortcut to muscles are in their fifties. It's easy to scoff at warnings when one is young, feeling strong and healthy, but it remains to be seen how these drug users' attitudes may change if it should develop that these compounds do produce a significant incidence of cancer of the liver or other organs in the long term.

chapter eight
ultimate possibilities

In the introduction to this book I alluded to several versatile athletes who had developed great strength with weight training and also were versatile performers at running, jumping, and throwing or wrestling. References to Gottfried Wuthrich ("Rolandow"), Donald Dinnie, and William B. Curtis are based on David P. Willoughby's carefully researched and fascinating book, *The Super Athletes* (A. S. Barnes & Company, 1970).

Earlier in this book I have mentioned other versatile strength athletes as examples of the possibilities of human strength as related to athletic achievements aside from Olympic or power lifting. There is something especially remarkable about athletes who excel in more than one demanding sport. Randy Matson is one example, a paragon of controlled power who not only set a world record in the shot put while at Texas A&M, but also was an outstanding varsity basketball player. Others include the men who won important championships as both shot-putters and weight lifters: Al Feuerbach, Bruce Wilhelm, and Sam Walker.

Then there is the amazingly versatile Brian Oldfield, a 6'5" giant weighing between 250 and 270 pounds who toyed with a 300-pound barbell in the televised "Superstars" competition, was the first man to put the 16-pound shot 75 feet, and did exceptionally well in a variety of unpracticed events at the Scottish Highland Games (Shades of Donald Dinnie!). Delighting the hearts of male chauvinists, Oldfield regularly outsprinted leading women sprinters, seemingly without really trying.

I have not discussed the possibilities of human strength and power in terms of specializing Olympic and power lifting champions, because that isn't what this book is about. But in concentrating on the strength and power possibilities of versatile weight trained athletes, two deserve more detailed mention.

One is Jon Cole, a throwback to the old-time strongman athlete who seemed to be able to do just about anything requiring coordinated power. Cole was a state (Arizona) Olympic lifting champion and a national power lifting champion. He also won the national AAU discus championship in 1969, beating another great weight-trained, record-setting platter spinner, L. J. Silvester. The same year Cole won the U.S. power lift title in the 242-pound class with a 745-pound squat, a 495-pound bench press, and a 765-pound dead lift.

At 5'11" and 240 pounds, Cole measured 51 inches around the chest, 38½ around the waist, 31½ around the thigh, 18½ at the calf, and had a flexed upper arm of 20½ inches.

In 1972 Cole ranked fourth in the world with a discus throw of 216 feet 3 inches and won the superheavyweight power lift title with an 865-pound squat, a 570-pound bench press, and an 820-pound dead lift, weighing 270 pounds. The same year he won the Arizona state Olympic lift title with a 430-pound press, a 340-pound snatch, and a 430-pound clean and jerk. Still later in 1972, at the Arizona state power lift meet, weighing 283, Cole

An old photo taken at Arizona State University shows Jon Cole about to release the discus. In 1969 Cole won the national AAU championship in the discus throw and the national power lifting title the same year. *(Photo by Charles Conley, courtesy of Arizona State University)*

squatted with 905 pounds, bench pressed 580 pounds, and dead lifted 885 pounds. At 283 pounds, his chest had increased to 56 inches, his thigh to 32 inches, and his flexed arm to 21½ inches, according to a report by Bruce Wilhelm in *Iron Man* magazine (June–July 1973).

An account of Jon Cole's great lifting and discus throwing fails to describe his versatility, however, for he had many other noteworthy achievements (presumably most of them made at about 240 pounds body weight):

40-yard dash, 4.6 seconds
100-yard dash, 10 seconds
16-pound shot put, 62 feet 10¼ inches
Javelin throw, 221 feet
Squat, 18 repetitions with 600 pounds
Press, 460 pounds overhead from shoulders (no clean)

For a combination of sprinting speed, throwing power in three events—shot, discus, and javelin—and lifting strength, it would be difficult to find a match for Jon Cole in recorded sports history.

In considering the ultimate combination of weight-trained power and versatile, truly all-around athletic performance, we have to look to the decathlon champions. As far as I know, they all train with weights. Bruce Jenner, one of the most highly publicized decathlon athletes, won the Olympic title in 1976 with a world record point score and has been pictured practicing heavy cleans. He was credited with a clean and jerk of 270 pounds. Bill Toomey, who won the Olympic decathlon in 1968, also with a record total at the time, could bench press 320 pounds.

Toomey and Jenner were ideal size decathlon athletes at around 6′1″–6′2″ and 190–195 pounds, but a man who preceded them in holding the world record, Russ Hodge, was bigger and stronger. In fact, Hodge's size—6′3″ and 220–225 pounds—was somewhat of a handicap in some of the events; the pole vault and 1,500-meter run, for example.

Jon Cole, about to ram a 400-pounds-plus barbell overhead, became one of the greatest all-around strength athletes of all time with such achievements as a discus throw of 216 feet 3 inches, a squat with 905 pounds, bench press with 580 pounds, and 10 seconds for running the 100-yard dash. *(Photo by Bruce Klemens)*

101

Russ Hodge, who set a world record in the decathlon without reaching his best in one of the ten events, could bench press 480 pounds and squat with 600 at a height of 6'3" and a weight of 225 pounds. He also ran 100 meters in 10.2 and 1,500 meters in 4:12.7, an incredible combination of strength, speed, and endurance. *(Photo courtesy of UCLA)*

But Hodge, who set a world record of 8,230 points in 1966, never seemed to achieve his full potential, primarily because of a series of unfortunate injuries. Compare, for example, his performances when he set the world record with his all-time best individual performances in the ten events that make up the decathlon:

World Record, 1966	Event	All-Time Personal Best
10.5	100 Meters	10.2
24'7¾"	Long Jump	25'2¾"
56'7¼"	Shot Put	60'10¾"
6'⅞"	High Jump	6'4"
48.9	400 Meters	47.9
15.2	Hurdles	14.6
165'5¾"	Discus	174'4"
13'5½"	Pole Vault	13'11¼"
211'7"	Javelin	212'3"
4:40.4	1,500 Meters	4:12.7

As the comparison shows, Hodge did not achieve a personal peak performance in one of the ten events when he set his world record, though he came close with the javelin.

When you consider Hodge's great all-around athletic ability, as shown by his performances in the decathlon events, in relation to his strength, as measured by weight lifting, he has to rank as one of the superathletes of all time. A tall man with what might be termed ideal proportions, Hodge was not nearly heavy enough to have the favorable lifting leverage possessed by weight lifting champions. But, nevertheless, he bench pressed 480 pounds and performed a deep squat with 600 pounds! Furthermore, he did a partial squat, almost parallel, with 775 pounds.

Those lifts, done by a man who set a world record in the decathlon without even doing his best in the ten track and field events, add up to a superathlete second to none. From this superathlete, quoted in *Power & Fitness* magazine, come some training tips that should be posted on the wall of every athletic training facility in the country:

103

Weight training is primarily to develop speed and strength. To me, speed and strength are synonymous.

Get most of your conditioning and endurance out on the track. Get your strength in the weight room.

Hodge also recommends that a person starting a weight training program spend the first two or three weeks just working with three sets of eight to ten repetitions in the exercises, not trying to lift heavy weights, to get the feel of the exercises, acquire muscle tone, and avoid injuries.

appendix: for additional information

I have consciously tried to refrain from writing in the arcane and esoteric terms so popular with authors in the "soft" sciences and pseudosciences. Such jargon is eagerly adopted by certain athletic trainers and hucksters who use it to overwhelm the uninitiated and naive. I have also deliberately refrained from erudite discussion of which muscles work when you do this or that, except where such discussion seemed absolutely necessary to understanding what the book is about—practical application of strength training for functional fitness. But if you want more detailed discussion of how to develop specific muscles; how to learn the Olympic lifts; how to train for power lifting; the difference between "fast twitch" and "slow twitch" muscles; how to train for running, jumping and throwing; nutrition; and the use of drugs in sports, I would recommend the following references, though a couple are somewhat overly positive about scientific "Truths" that are likely to be disproved as time passes:

Gardner, J. B., and J. G. Purdy. *Computerized Running Training Programs.* Los Altos, Calif.: TAFNEWS Press, 1970.

Hatfield, F. C., and M. L. Krotee. *Personalized Weight Training for Fitness and Athletics.* Dubuque, Iowa: Kendall/Hunt Publishing Company, 1978.

Hatfield, F. C. *Powerlifting, A Scientific Approach.* Chicago: Contemporary Books, Inc., 1981.

Murray, J. *Inside Weight Lifting and Weight Training.* Chicago: Contemporary Books, Inc., 1977.

———. *Inside Bodybuilding.* Chicago: Contemporary Books, Inc., 1978.

Todd, T., and D. Hoover. *Fitness for Athletes*. Chicago: Contemporary Books, Inc., 1978.

Track Technique (Quarterly). Track & Field News, P.O. Box 296, Los Altos, Calif. 94022

Willoughby, D. P. *The Super Athletes*. Cranbury, N.J.: A. S. Barnes and Company, 1970.

In addition to the publications listed above, a number of periodicals either regularly or occasionally publish articles on weight training by athletes. Over the years *Strength & Health* has reported on many outstanding weight trained athletes, and two relative newcomers in the field—*Power & Fitness* and *Bodypower*—have published instructive and inspirational articles on weight training for athletes. *Iron Man* magazine occasionally includes information on weight trained athletes other than lifters and bodybuilders, and so does *Muscle & Fitness*—though the latter publication focuses on bodybuilding and only features the nonbodybuilder on rare occasions.

index

D

Davis, Dave, 12
Dead lift, 12
Deltoid muscles, exercises for
    strengthening of, 63
Diet fads, 95
Dinnie, Donald, x–xi, 97, 98
Discus throwers
    dumbbell exercises for, 63
    weight training for, 46, 77–78
Dolegiewicz, Bishop, 46–48,
    84–85
Donlon, Jim, 44
Downing, Brian, 46
Drugs, 96
    and athletic performance, 5
Dumbbells
    exercises using, 62–64
    use of, to build strength and
        power, 4

E

Emrich, Clyde, 29, 30
Exercise equipment
    for weight training, 7–8
    mail order sources for, 8
Exercise machines, 7
    disadvantages of, 4
Exercises
    for abdominal muscles, 49–51
    extension, for the triceps,
        66–68
    for fingers, 59–61
    for hands, 59–61
    for legs, 56–57
    for the neck, 58
    for strengthening lower legs,
        51–56

    for wrists, 59–61
    using dumbbells, 62–64

F

Feuerbach, Al, 12, 98
Fingers, exercises for
    strengthening, 59–61
Fitness for Athletes (Todd and
    Hoover), 106
Flying exercise, 63–64, 77
Football players
    and bench pressing, 25
    planning effective program
        for, 38
    use of heavy weights in
        parallel squats, 33
    weight training for, 10, 77–78
Francis, Beverly, 28, 29, 35, 37
Frederick, Jane, 28

G

Gardner, J. B., 106
General conditioning, 90–92
Glance, Harvey, 26
Griffin, Lorna, 29, 35
Gymnasts, weight training for,
    82

H

Hackenschmidt, George, x, 58
Hammer throwers
    key exercises for, 69–70
    use of heavy weights in
        parallel squats, 33
    weight training for, 77–78
Hamstrings, exercises for, 56
Hands, exercises for
    strengthening, 59–61

Neck, exercises for
strengthening, 58
Neeld, Dave, 86
Nutrition, 94–95
and athletic performance, 5

O

Oerter, Al, 26–27
Off-season training, 40
Oldfield, Brian, 12, 98
Olympic bar, 8
Olympic lifts, 12
Olympic snatch, 12

P

Parallel squat, 30–35
for basketball player, 39
for hammer throwers, 69
logical progression with, 72
reasons for selection of, 11
for shot putter, 39
for wrestler, 39
Payton, Walter, 30
Pectoral muscles, exercises for
strengthening of, 63–64
Percentage system, 85. *See also*
Cycle approach
*Personalized Weight Training for
Fitness and Athletics*
(Hatfield), 106
Peterson, John, 22
Pole vaulters
use of biceps curls, 53–56
weight training for, 83
Power & Fitness, 106
Power clean
for basketball players, 38, 39
for hammer throwers, 69

logical progression with, 72
procedure for doing, 14–22
reasons for selection of, 10–12
similarity of, to olympic
lifting, 12
Power zones, 30
Pressing weights overhead,
71–75
Pseudoscience, 5, 7
Pullover, 69
Pulse rate
elevation of, during exercise, 2
maintenance of, during weight
training, 2
Purdy, J. G., 106
Push-ups, without special
equipment, 3–4

R

Racquet sports, weight training
for, 81–82
Racquetball, 81–82
Repetitions, definition of, 9
Reverse curls, 59, 61, 76
Richards, Bob, xi–xii
Rise-on-toes, 76
Rohn, Don, 26
Rope skipping, and aerobic
conditioning, 7
Running
integration of, with weight
training, 5, 92–93
and pulse rate, 2
training for, 5, 7

S

Set, definition of, 9
Shot putter